Australian
GEOGRAPHIC

AUSTRALIA'S
MOST
DANGEROUS

CREATURES

On land and at sea
Identification and first aid

Species text by Kelvin Aitken, Ian Connellan,
Dr Peter Fenner, Steve K. Wilson and Paul Zborowski
Additional text by Ian Connellan
First aid information courtesy of St John Ambulance Australia
and the Australian Red Cross

First-edition text by Carl Edmonds,
Julian White and Paul Zborowski

EMERGENCY PHONE NUMBERS

NAME: _____

ADDRESS: _____

_____

NEXT OF KIN: _____

PHONE NUMBER: _____

Poisons Information Centre:

13 11 26 from anywhere in Australia

The Poisons Information Centre can give advice on bites and stings, any time, from anywhere in Australia.

Ambulance:

Dial **000**

Always call an ambulance in times of emergency. The DRSABCD Action Plan can be found on page 182 of this book.

HOSPITAL: DOCTOR: 24-HOUR CHEMIST:

ABOUT THE
CONTRIBUTORS

KELVIN AITKEN
Shark text and photographs

KELVIN IS A PROFESSIONAL photographer and cinematographer specialising in marine wildlife. Over 25 years he has captured images of rare and exotic animals found in all of the Earth's oceans from the polar regions to the tropics, in habitats as diverse as tidal pools and the deep ocean.

Kelvin is the founder of image library Marine Themes. His work has been widely published and broadcast: in magazines, including AUSTRALIAN GEOGRAPHIC, *Time* and *National Geographic*; in books from major international publishing houses; and on digital platforms including television documentaries and scientific research papers.

DR PETER FENNER
Marine creatures text

UK-TRAINED PETER has practised medicine in Australia for more than three decades, specialising in occupational health and medicine. An acknowledged expert on marine stingers, he is a former long-serving honorary medical officer for Surf Life Saving Australia, and a former chairman of the International Surf Lifesaving Association's medical panel.

Peter was appointed Associate Professor of James Cook University's (JCU) School of Medicine in 2000, and Associate Professor of JCU's School of Health & Science in 2001. His publications include *The Marine Stinger Guide and Venomous and Poisonous Marine Animals: A Medical and Biological Handbook*, as well as many contributions to professional journals.

STEVE K. WILSON
Snake and crocodile text and photographs

———

STEVE IS AN AWARD-WINNING Australian herpetologist, naturalist, photographer and author based in southern Queensland. Over nearly four decades Steve has compiled one of the most comprehensive image libraries of Australian and international reptiles. He's written and photographed several stories for the AUSTRALIAN GEOGRAPHIC journal, and has authored and co-authored several books, including *Complete Guide to Reptiles of Australia* (with Gerry Swan) and *Australian Lizards – A Natural History.*

A freelance wildlife consultant and naturalist tour guide, Steve also has a keen interest in, and fine knowledge of, birds and mammals, invertebrates and botany. He's worked as an information officer for the Queensland Museum since 1986, a role that sees him identifying specimens brought in by members of the public, and telling people of the need to conserve Australia's unique biological heritage.

PAUL ZBOROWSKI
Spider and insect text and photographs

———

PAUL, WHO CONTRIBUTED the insects and spiders chapters to the first edition of *Australia's Most Dangerous*, is a qualified entomologist with several decades' experience of field research of insects and related creatures in tropical habitats. His studies have taken him to West Africa, Sumatra, Borneo, New Guinea, the Cape York wilderness, and throughout the Wet Tropics World Heritage Area in northern Queensland, which is close to his home.

Paul owns and runs the Close-up Photo Library, which specialises in images of insects, plants, fungi and other rainforest denizens. He has produced reference works, field guides and children's books, and his writing and photography have been widely published in magazines and journals. He also works as a specialist consultant to documentary filmmakers.

IAN CONNELLAN
Editor, and author of additional text

———

IAN IS AN EDITOR, writer and photographer, a former editor-in-chief of AUSTRALIAN GEOGRAPHIC and a former trustee and advisory councillor of the Australian Geographic Society. Over the past 25 years he's written countless articles, co-authored several *Lonely Planet* travel guides and commissioned or edited dozens of non-fiction books. He specialises in travel photography and his work is in the Lonely Planet Images collection, now part of Getty Images. Based in Hobart, Ian and his partner now run the specialist travel company Curious Traveller.

✚ **First aid information courtesy of St John Ambulance Australia and the Australian Red Cross.**

CONTRIBUTORS

AUSTRALIA'S
MOST
DANGEROUS

First published in 2017
Australian Geographic, an imprint of
Bauer Media Ltd, 54 Park Street, Sydney NSW 2000
Telephone 02 9263 9813 **Fax** 02 8116 9377
Email editorial@ausgeo.com.au
australiangeographic.com.au

National Library of Australia Cataloguing-in-Publication entry
Creator: Aitken, Kelvin, author.

Title: Australia's most dangerous / species text by Kelvin Aitken,
Dr Peter Fenner, Steve K. Wilson and Paul Zborowski; first aid infor-
mation courtesy of St John Ambulance Australia and the Australian
Red Cross; additional text by Ian Connellan; edited by Ian Connellan,
Chrissie Goldrick and Karen McGhee; designed by Mike Ellott and
Andrew Burns.

ISBN: 9781742457475 (paperback)

Subjects: Dangerous animals--Australia.
First aid in illness and injury--Australia.

Other Creators/Contributors:
Fenner, Peter, author
Wilson, Steve K., author
Zborowski, Paul, author
Connellan, Ian, author, editor
Goldrick, Chrissie, editor
McGhee, Karen, editor
Ellott, Mike, book designer
Burns, Andrew, book designer
St John Ambulance Australia
Australian Geographic Pty Ltd, issuing body

Dewey Number: 591.650994

Chief Executive Officer, Bauer Media Group Paul Dykzeul
Publisher, Bauer Media Specialist Division Jo Runciman

Printed in China by C & C Offset Printing Co., Ltd.

Previous pages
Page 1 Redback spider
Page 2 Great white shark
Page 5 Desert scorpion

CONTENTS

6 About the Contributors **10** Foreword **12** Introduction

Broad-headed snake

LAND

Oceanic whitetip Shark

SEA

16 VENOMOUS SNAKES
18 Snake features
20 How antivenom is made
21 Snake scales
22 Brown snakes
26 Black snakes
30 Small-eyed snakes
32 Taipans
36 Death adders
40 Broad-headed snakes
44 Copperheads
47 Rough-scaled snake
48 Tiger snake
50 Snake safety
51 10 most venomous snakes
52 **Snakebite first aid**

54 SPIDERS AND OTHER ARACHNIDS
56 Funnel-web spiders
62 Redback spider
64 Mouse spiders
66 Wolf spiders
68 World's deadliest spiders
70 White-tailed spiders
71 More likely to die from
72 Black house spiders
74 **Spider bite first aid**
76 Scorpions and centipedes
78 Paralysis tick
80 Biggest dangers on Australian land

82 INSECTS
84 Bees
86 Bull ants
88 Stinging caterpillars
89 Hairy caterpillars
90 Paper wasps
92 Mosquitoes
95 Prevention is better than cure

96 MAMMALS
96 Platypus

100 SHARKS
102 Bull shark
104 Great white shark
106 Shark attacks by numbers
108 Oceanic whitetip shark
109 Reduce risk
110 Tiger shark
112 Shortfin mako shark
113 Bronze whaler shark

114 CROCODILES
116 Saltwater and freshwater

120 JELLYFISH & THEIR KIN
122 Box jellyfish
124 Irukandji
127 Jimble
128 Bluebottles
132 Other jellyfish

137 VENOMOUS FISHES
138 Stonefishes
141 Scorpionfishes
142 Catfishes
146 Other venomous fishes

148 DANGEROUS MARINE ANIMALS
150 Blue-ringed octopus
153 Cone shells
155 Sea snakes
156 Stinging hydroids
161 Fire corals
162 Stingrays
166 Bristle worms
168 Sponges
171 Common octopuses
173 Eels
175 Gropers
176 Sea anemones
178 Sea urchins

180 First Aid
182 DRSABCD action plan
184 Anaphylaxis
185 Bites & stings
186 Severe bleeding
187 Shock & trauma
188 General index
193 Scientific name index
198 Photographers' credits

FOREWORD

B ORN AND RAISED IN AFRICA, I was well aware of, and familiar with, the presence of potentially dangerous wild animals, big and small. Thus my relocation to Australia some years ago didn't instil in me the usual fears that some new arrivals have of coming face-to-face with the myriad potentially dangerous creatures that are reputed to abound on, and off, the shores of this island continent. In fact, considering my chosen specialty, herpetology (the study of reptiles and amphibians), I was elated to find myself delivered into the midst of this new place of wondrous wilderness and wildlife. In some ways Australia is similar to my old home, but in many others, so very different. I was excited at the prospect of rediscovery. Not only was there somewhere in the region of 170 land dwelling species of snake recorded (of which about 70 per cent are venomous – 30 species potentially fatal to humans) and 32 venomous sea snakes, but there were many other venomous creatures of which I had only minimal knowledge, including a fascinating assortment of spiders, insects and other invertebrates, and marine animals.

Through my work as a herpetologist and wildlife documentary and adventure filmmaker, I have, on numerous occasions, unwittingly placed myself in harm's way – especially where venomous reptiles are concerned. This has sometimes resulted in trips to hospital for urgent medical attention, or, in extreme situations, emergency self-administered treatment in the field.

And although the well-informed, everyday traveller/explorer/camper/hiker is unlikely to be confronted with a similar scenario, it's important to appreciate that accidents can happen, and the potential for an encounter with a dangerous animal in the wild really exists here in Australia. It is this possibility, however slight, that makes this book, *Australia's Most Dangerous*, so valuable. When encountering a dangerous animal two things are of utmost importance. First, identification of the animal concerned. Second, correct first aid treatment if envenomation has taken place. It is understandable that to the average person all snakes basically look the same, as do many spiders and the smaller sea creatures. If bitten by a snake or spider, or even some obscure sea-dwelling creature, being able to identify the

Austin Stevens handles a subadult alligator in the Florida Everglades.

species will be of great advantage to any lay person, or a medical team faced with the treatment of injuries. From bites and stings delivered by a variety of Australian insects and invertebrate species, to the vast array of potentially dangerous reptiles, to the largest ocean predators, as well as anything in between, this book outlines all the facts and figures, from clear photo identification to the most up-to-date treatment applications and emergency procedures.

Although it's a fact that wild animals, dangerous or otherwise, will generally avoid confrontation with humans, accidents do occur. Having experienced the frightening scenario of an 'in the field' traumatic emergency brought about by a dangerous animal encounter personally, I would strongly advise that every Australian traveller be armed with the potentially life-saving knowledge contained in this book.

And finally, remember that each and every wonderful wild creature that evolved to exist on this planet, in one way or another, forms an intricate link in the chain that binds all of the natural world together – and that includes us.

Austin J. Stevens
www.facebook.com/austinstevensadventurer

INTRODUCTION

FROM AN OUTDOOR ENTHUSIAST'S perspective, Australia is a magnificent country to explore. Across the country's many climatic zones, a vast array of habitats on land and at sea support animal cohorts that are, in many cases, found nowhere else in the world.

But among these creatures are some that cause a good deal of alarm, even fear, for Australians and overseas visitors keen to enjoy the great outdoors. This book – like its first-edition predecessor – is intended to help people overcome those fears, through improving knowledge and appreciation of Australia's dangerous animals.

The book's species descriptions are designed to assist with animal identification. They include scientific and common names (the latter as always are problematic, because animals are often known by multiple common names), are illustrated with colour photographs and include distribution maps. The book's authors have long experience of these creatures and are, in most cases, experts in their fields.

While an unfavourable encounter with any of the animals described is extremely unlikely, up-to-date first aid information is crucial. We encourage all readers to undertake a first aid course: knowing what to do in case of emergency is vital and usually involves simple information that everyone in the community should know. The Australian Red Cross and St John Ambulance Service both offer excellent first aid training. Visit *redcross.org.au/firstaid* or *stjohn.org.au/first-aid-training*.

The animals described in the book are, in most cases, beautiful and without exception remarkable. All have fascinating evolutionary histories that have brought them, in the present, to their positions in the ecosystems they occupy. Some are apex predators and their role is critical to the animals that surround them and on which they prey. Almost all can be seen, and enjoyed, in safety.

The dangers of encounters with these animals are often exaggerated, to their – and our – detriment. Usually a few simple cautions are enough to safeguard humans against the risks, and allow us to enjoy the rewards of seeing these fabulous creatures in their natural environment.

A note on scientific names

An animal's **scientific**, or Latin, name is bestowed in accordance with a relatively simple set of rules. The names are binomial – in two parts: the first indicating the animal's genus, and the second its species. The name is written in italics, with the first letter of the generic name always capitalised, and the specific name all in lower case. Hence *Crocodylus porosus* – the estuarine, or saltwater, crocodile.

In some cases, an entry will refer to several animals of the same genus, but not to them specifically: in such cases the abbreviation 'spp.' is used. Hence *Anemonia* spp. – multiple species of the sea anemone genus *Anemonia*.

Above genus, animals are divided into progressively larger groups: genera (plural of genus) into families, families into orders, orders into classes, and classes into phyla.

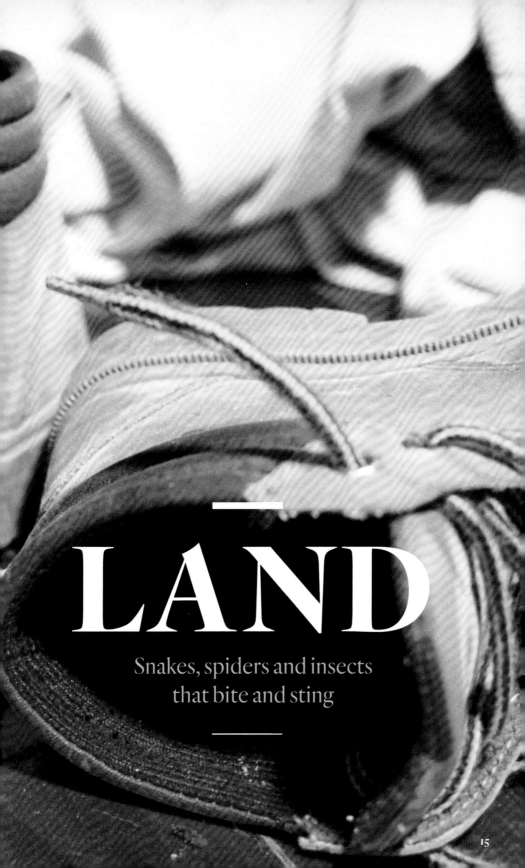

LAND

Snakes, spiders and insects
that bite and sting

——

Eastern brown snake

WE SHARE OUR CONTINENT WITH ABOUT 170 DIFFERENT SPECIES OF LAND SNAKE, SOME OF WHICH COME EQUIPPED WITH MORE TOXIC VENOM THAN ANY OTHER SNAKES IN THE WORLD.

VENOMOUS SNAKES

ABOUT 3000 SNAKEBITES are reported in Australia each year, up to 500 of which result in antivenom treatment. The long-term national average of 2–3 snakebite deaths per year appears to be falling.

In contrast, World Health Organization estimates suggest there are about 2.4 million snakebite envenomations worldwide each year, resulting in 94,000–125,000 deaths. Those most affected are subsistence farmers in Africa and South-East Asia, who have poor access to healthcare and antivenoms.

About 70 per cent of Australia's 170 or so different types of land snake are venomous, about 25–30 of which are considered capable of fatal envenomations. The widespread eastern, or common, brown snake (see page 25) is thought to be responsible for more than half of all fatal snakebites in Australia.

Most of Australia's venomous snakes, and those classified as potentially deadly, belong to the family Elapidae, which also includes – in other countries – the cobras and mambas. The remaining venomous species are in the family Colubridae.

With few exceptions, these animals prefer to move away if humans approach and it's unusual to stumble upon them in the bush. If you do encounter a snake, the most sensible thing to do is step back and watch it go about its business.

25+
SPECIES
2-3
DEATHS

AUSTRALIA HAS AT LEAST **25 SPECIES** OF DEADLY SNAKE BUT **ONLY ABOUT 3 DEATHS** A YEAR FROM SNAKEBITE

SNAKE FEATURES

what is snake venom?

The fangs of a red-bellied black snake.

The primary purpose of snake venom is to immobilise prey, but from the human experience it's more significant when a snake bites to defend itself.

Venom is modified saliva. It is stored in venom glands located in the upper jaw behind the eye, and connected by ducts to either deeply grooved or hollow fangs. It is not a single toxin, but a complex cocktail. The balance of components varies between snake species and has differing effects on the body of the victim.

Myotoxins attack muscle tissue. When injected into prey, these may act to aid its digestion. In humans they can cause severe muscle destruction and may lead to acute kidney failure.

Haemotoxins act on the blood by interfering with normal clotting, including platelet production, or by destroying blood cells, particularly red blood cells. Haemotoxins are a component of most snake venoms to varying degrees. They trigger complex processes that may have coagulant or anticoagulant effects.

Neurotoxins disrupt the transmission of information in the nervous system by inhibiting the release of transmitters from nerve endings. They are often the most lethal components of a snake venom, and, because most of their action is centred where a nerve impulse is transmitted to a voluntary muscle, can cause paralysis.

It is worth noting the difference between venoms and poisons. Poisons are toxic when swallowed, whereas a venom is injected. For this reason, we refer to venomous rather than poisonous snakes.

Snakebite biomechanics

Snake fangs are modified teeth, shaped through evolution for the specialised task of delivering venom. Some are hollow like hypodermic needles. Others are grooved like miniature aqueducts. Depending on the type of snake, they can be located at the front or rear of the mouth.

Most Australian venomous snakes belong to the group known as elapids. They have small, fixed fangs at the front of the mouth and attached to the maxilla (upper jaw). They usually have four fangs – two in use and two in reserve on each side – at any one time. When they bite, masseter muscles at the rear of their mouth contract and squeeze the venom gland, forcing venom through a duct, into the fang and then into the prey.

Australia has six species of colubrid snake, only one of which (the brown tree snake) has fangs at the back of the mouth and a less sophisticated venom-delivery system. Its fangs are grooved and its venom is generally less potent than that of elapids.

The pit vipers and true vipers – which aren't found in Australia – are the venomous snakes with the longest and most sophisticated fangs. These are hollow, about three times the length of elapids' fangs, and are the only teeth on the upper jaw of these snakes' mouths. They can penetrate deeply during a bite and are capable of injecting large amounts of venom.

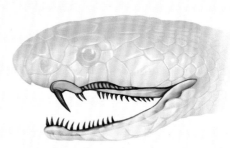

ELAPIDS
More than 60 per cent of Australia's snake species are elapids, which have fangs located near the front of the mouth. Because the fangs are small, elapids need to hang on when they bite, at least briefly, to be able to inject their venom.

COLUBRIDS
These are the dominant snakes in most parts of the world. Australia is a notable exception, having just six species, all found in the country's north or north-east. One of those species, the brown tree snake, has small fangs at the rear of the mouth.

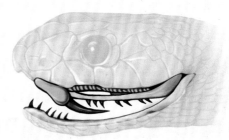

VIPERS
The medium to very large fangs of vipers are mounted on a hinged bone at the front of the mouth, which allows them to be folded back against the roof of the mouth when not in use.

Note: These images illustrate the mechanics of snake fangs and are not to be used for the purpose of snake identification.

Collecting venom through 'milking' involves persuading a snake to bite a rubber membrane stretched over a vial in which the venom is collected before being freeze-dried.

How antivenom is made

NTIVENOMS ARE designed for treating venomous bites and stings and can be a critical response to snakebite. When used in conjunction with rapid and appropriate first aid (see pages 52–53 and 180–187), a victim's survival chances will be extremely high.

To produce these life-saving substances, venom is 'milked' from captive snakes. Just a few drops of venom – usually a clear yellowish liquid – are extracted from a snake each time it is milked. This is desiccated under a vacuum or freeze-dried, forming crystals. Very small quantities are then regularly injected into large test animals over lengthy periods of time.

Horses are often used for this because of their size and ease of handling. It causes them no ill effects and individuals can be used again and again. Repeated low doses will trigger a horse's immune system to produce antibodies to counteract the venom of whichever particular snake species is used. A horse may, for example, be repeatedly dosed with tiger snake venom. Its blood is collected, and from the plasma the component containing antibodies generated by the horse to counteract the venom is extracted. When injected into a tiger snake bite victim, these antibodies recognise and neutralise the venom.

There are five different groups of Australian snake venom, each named after a particular species. These are used to create 'monovalent' antivenoms, which each target a single venom type. Several related species may share a venom type and a swab at the bite site will determine which it is and the appropriate antivenom to use against it. For this reason, you shouldn't wash a bite site during first aid treatment.

The five monovalent antivenoms are:

Tiger snake, which is effective against tiger snakes, copperheads, broad-headed snakes and rough-scaled snakes.

Taipan is specifically for the taipans.

Death adder is specific to death adders.

Black snake targets various black snake species including red-bellied blacks and mulga, or king brown, snakes.

Brown snake neutralises the venoms of all brown snake species.

A sixth **'polyvalent'** antivenom combines several monovalents. This is used when a venom type cannot be identified or a victim's symptoms are progressing so rapidly there is no time to determine the appropriate monovalent antivenom.

Snake scale terminology

ACCURATE IDENTIFICATION of snakes often relies on examining their scales. The most important features are the number of midbody scale rows and whether the anal and subcaudal scales are divided or undivided.

Midbody scales are counted around the body, roughly at the mid-section. Begin counting on one side of the broad ventral scales and follow a diagonal line of scales until reaching the other side. The ventral row is not included.

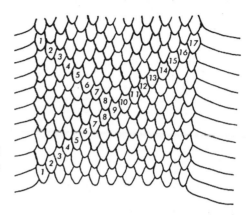

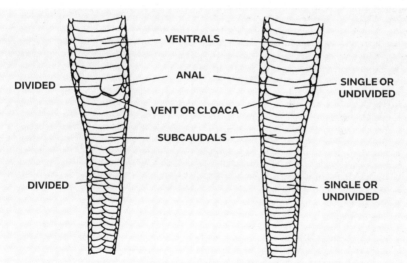

VENTRALS

ANAL

DIVIDED

SINGLE OR UNDIVIDED

VENT OR CLOACA

SUBCAUDALS

DIVIDED

SINGLE OR UNDIVIDED

THE ANAL SCALE covers the cloaca or vent. It may be a single large scale, or it may have a longitudinal suture dividing it into two.

Subcaudal scales run beneath the tail. If undivided, they form a complete series very much like the broad ventral scales. If divided, they each have an oblique suture creating a double series. Some species of snakes have all subcaudal scales divided, others have all single, and several species exhibit a combination of both conditions.

All snakes are protected and should not be handled without appropriate permits. Handling snakes also poses obvious hazards and should only be done under expert supervision.

Speckled brown snake

BROWN SNAKES

GENUS *Pseudonaja*

DUGITE *Pseudonaja affinis*
STRAP-SNOUTED BROWN SNAKE *Pseudonaja aspidorhyncha*
SPECKLED BROWN SNAKE *Pseudonaja guttata*
PENINSULA BROWN SNAKE *Pseudonaja inframacula*
INGRAM'S BROWN SNAKE *Pseudonaja ingrami*
WESTERN BROWN SNAKE; GWARDAR; MENGDEN'S
BROWN SNAKE *Pseudonaja mengdeni*
RINGED BROWN SNAKE *Pseudonaja modesta*
NORTHERN BROWN SNAKE *Pseudonaja nuchalis*
EASTERN (COMMON) BROWN SNAKE *Pseudonaja textilis*

DESPITE THEIR COMMON name, brown snakes exhibit a
bewildering array of colours, from brown to brick-red, cream
and black. Individuals may have prominent bands, scattered
black scales or oblique herringbone markings. Distinctive shared
features include a narrow head, moderately large eyes and orange to
pink ventral flecks. Juveniles have a prominent black cap on the head
and broad black band across the neck. Mid-body scale rows range
from 17 to 21; the anal and subcaudal scales are divided, although the
first few subcaudal scales may be entire.

Brown snakes occur Australia-wide in warm, dry, open habitats.
Land clearing has favoured these snakes, which thrive on farmlands
and around the margins of towns and cities. They feed on a variety
of vertebrates, from lizards, snakes (including their own species) and
frogs, to birds and mammals. Introduced house mice are particular
favourites. Brown snakes lay eggs, producing up to 38 per clutch.

These snakes have a nervous disposition and are unlikely to attack
but will respond rapidly and aggressively when threatened, raising
the fore-body in an S-shape or flattening it to form a hood and
gaping the mouth. They may strike repeatedly.

The venom is highly toxic but only small quantities are produced
and delivered via short fangs. It is difficult for these snakes to bite
through clothing, and up to two-thirds of bites may not inject
venom. Envenomation symptoms include headache, dizziness,
nausea, vomiting, intense abdominal pain, reduced ability or inability
of the blood to clot, and occasionally convulsions or paralysis. There
is usually little or no pain, swelling or tissue damage at the bite site.

Eastern brown snake

SPECKLED BROWN SNAKE
Pseudonaja guttata (Previous page)

With a distribution spanning central
Queensland and a small part of the
eastern Northern Territory, the speckled
brown snake is restricted to treeless grassy
plains on cracking clay soils. It's a
particularly notable inhabitant of the
cracked black soils of central Queensland
and the Barkly Tableland, where it
avoids extreme daytime temperatures by
sheltering in deep cracks and the burrows
of small mammals.

Not much is known of the venom of
this species, but it's thought to be just as
toxic as that of other brown snakes.

EASTERN BROWN SNAKE
Pseudonaja textilis

This, the largest brown snake species, occasionally exceeds 2m in length. It is abundant across vast tracts of eastern Australia, with a distribution that extends from Cape York, in northern Queensland, down throughout the eastern mainland states and into parts of the Northern Territory and South Australia. This coincides with many of Australia's most populated areas, which is probably one reason why it's the snake species responsible for more human fatalities in Australia than any other.

It has a reputation for being aggressive, although experiments reveal it prefers to avoid conflict and is reluctant to bite, except under extreme provocation. This snake is one native species that has benefited from the spread of agriculture and pastoralism across mainland Australia. Thriving on introduced rats and mice, its numbers have risen since European settlement.

Its venom contains a range of powerful toxins affecting the nerves, heart, kidneys and blood and can cause paralysis and excessive bleeding.

WESTERN BROWN SNAKE
Pseudonaja mengdeni

Also known commonly as Mengden's brown snake or the gwardar, genetic studies have shown this to be one of several brown snake species found in western parts of the country. It occurs across South Australia, the Northern Territory and Western Australia.

Thanks to numerous colour forms, western browns are among Australia's most variable snakes. They can be light-brown to red and almost black on the upper body with a range of patterns. The belly, however, is always a lighter colour, from cream–yellow to orange or even grey, with dark blotches. Western species are reportedly not as aggressive as the eastern brown although their venom is just as potent and these snakes will certainly strike if provoked.

Western brown snake

25

BLACK SNAKES

GENUS *Pseudechis*

MULGA (KING BROWN) SNAKE *Pseudechis australis*
SPOTTED MULGA SNAKE *Pseudechis butleri*
COLLETT'S SNAKE *Pseudechis colletti*
SPOTTED (BLUE-BELLIED) BLACK SNAKE *Pseudechis guttatus*
PAPUAN BLACK SNAKE *Pseudechis papuanus*
RED-BELLIED BLACK SNAKE *Pseudechis porphyriacus*
WESTERN PYGMY MULGA SNAKE *Pseudechis weigeli*
EASTERN DWARF MULGA SNAKE *Pseudechis pailsii*

THIS LARGE AND DIVERSE group includes snakes ranging in adult size from about 1m to more than 2m. They generally have broad heads and relatively small eyes, and, despite the name, few are black. Several are speckled or blotched and the most widespread, the mulga snake, is brown. Scales are smooth and glossy, in 17–19 mid-body rows, and in most species the subcaudal scales are mostly divided, with the first 20 per cent single. In pygmy and dwarf mulga snakes, however, they are all single.

This group occurs throughout most of mainland Australia, in habitats as diverse as temperate wetlands, desert sand dunes, tropical rainforests and tropical savannahs. Most species are active by day or night according to temperature. The group is unusual in exhibiting two reproduction modes. Most species lay eggs, producing clutches of up to 19, but the red-bellied black is a live-bearer.

When threatened, these snakes flatten their necks and fore-bodies and hiss loudly. Being quite thick-set they are generally clumsy. Venom does not appear to affect nerves so paralysis is unlikely. It seems instead to focus on blood and tissue such as muscles. Muscle destruction can mimic paralysis and lead to renal failure; blood clotting is severely affected and localised pain and swelling may be severe.

Mulga (king brown) snake

Red-bellied black snake

MULGA (KING BROWN) SNAKE
Pseudechis australis
(Previous page)

One of Australia's largest venomous snakes, it can reach an average 2m in length with a heavy build. Its colour is variable, from brown to rich reddish-brown. Scales have paler bases and darker edges, creating a netted pattern. Mid-body scales are in 17 rows. Its maximum length is 1.5m over most of its range, although it is often longer than 2m across the north, reaching 2.8m.

This species' common names are deceptive: it's found across much of Australia, well beyond mulga zones and is not allied to the brown snakes. Its venom is less toxic than many dangerous Australian snakes but it bites with a chewing action, has large fangs, and produces the highest venom yield.

Collett's snake

RED-BELLIED BLACK SNAKE
Pseudechis porphyriacus

The red-bellied black snake is sleek, shiny and black with an obvious red ventral colour that extends onto its lower flanks. Whether moving or at rest, the bright red is clearly visible. This contrasts with the much smaller eastern small-eyed snake (*Cryptophis nigrescens*), which has the pink colouration wholly confined to the belly and not visible unless the snake rears or is handled (see page 30). Red-bellied blacks have 17 mid-body scale rows and grow to nearly 2m.

The species' distribution extends from the south-eastern mainland to north-eastern Queensland, mainly near watercourses and in moist habitats such as tropical rainforests. They are extremely placid snakes, and for those with an eye for beauty in nature, the sight of a large, shiny red-bellied black sunning itself quietly on a creek bank is an unforgettable spectacle.

The species feeds on a variety of vertebrates including lizards, snakes, mammals and fish. Frogs are a favourite, and unfortunately the species' numbers have crashed due to attempted predation on the poisonous introduced cane toad. Any species that habitually takes frogs is at serious risk as toads continue to spread. However, there is evidence of a recovery in some parts of south-eastern Queensland, where red-bellied blacks are once again common in areas where toads have been established for decades.

COLLETT'S SNAKE
Pseudechis colletti

Distinctively patterned and often regarded as one of Australia's most stunningly marked snakes, this species has cream, pink to bright red bands or blotches on a grey to red-brown background. Mid-body scales are in 19 rows.

It's restricted to open plains of cracking clay soils vegetated with Mitchell grass (*Astrebla* spp.) in inland Queensland. With little or no tree cover the only shelter sites are within deep soil cracks.

Collett's snakes are secretive and rarely seen but have long been popular with reptile keepers, so any bites are likely to occur through handling.

SMALL-EYED SNAKES

GENUS *Cryptophis*

EASTERN SMALL-EYED SNAKE
Cryptophis nigrescens

THE EASTERN small-eyed snake is a glossy black snake with a pink belly. It has a flattened head with a squared snout and small black eyes. Mid-body scales are in 15 rows and anal and subcaudal scales are single. It normally grows to 50cm, although larger individuals can be found.

Because of its colouration, this species is often mistaken for a juvenile red-bellied black snake. On eastern small-eyed snakes, however, the belly colour is almost wholly confined to the ventral scales and cannot be seen unless the snake rears or is turned over. The overall effect is a black-coloured snake. On red-bellied black snakes, ventral colours extend onto the lower flanks so the red and black combination is clearly visible whether the snake is moving or at rest.

Eastern small-eyed snakes live in east Australian forests and heaths. They are nocturnal, sheltering by day under rocks and logs. They give birth to litters of up to eight live young and feed on small vertebrates, particularly lizards and frogs but also other snakes including their own kind. Eastern small-eyed snakes are extremely secretive but if provoked will flatten the body, thrash wildly and readily bite when handled.

Evidence suggests this snake's venom toxicity varies geographically. Bite symptoms range from no effects to renal failure, with one recorded fatality in Queensland. Some venom components continue attacking muscle, including the heart, for days after envenomation.

SNAKE LESSON
Hands-on experience has been the best preparation for Steve K. Wilson's role since 1986 – educating the public about snakes for the Queensland Museum.

1ST PERSON

New species first bite

Steve K. Wilson finds out the hard way that all snakebites should be taken seriously.

IN 1979 I HAD a rare opportunity to photograph a new snake species collected by museum colleagues at Lake Cronin, in southern Western Australia. The snake clearly belonged to the family Elapidae, the dominant group of Australian venomous snakes. It had a broad black head, pale eyes and matte-brown body. It was unlike any other known species and quite a treat for a herpetologist and photographer!

Unfortunately, it also took a dim view of posing for photos and, as I moved in for a close-up, bit my finger. Stupidly, I assumed it was only 'mildly' venomous and kept taking pictures.

Within 15 minutes I knew something was seriously wrong as I developed a blinding headache. By the time I reached hospital 40 minutes later I was vomiting and the headache had intensified. According to the hospital report my urine contained blood, and my blood coagulation profile was abnormal, with a greatly reduced clotting ability. There was no prospect of sampling surface venom to determine the appropriate antivenom. With clear signs of envenomation and knowing that this new species was completely untested, hospital staff administered an ampoule of polyvalent antivenom.

During the next 10 hours I began feeling better, but my blood was slower to recover. It was 24 hours before I was released from intensive care.

The snake is now known as the Lake Cronin snake (*Paroplocephalus atriceps*), a rare species related to the eastern Australian broad-headed snakes (*Hoplocephalus* spp.)

The moral of the story? Never underestimate the seriousness of a snakebite. Always apply first aid and seek medical help immediately, no matter how minor you think the bite may be. To trivialise a bite that turned out to be extremely significant was the greatest blunder of my career.

Coastal taipan

TAIPANS

GENUS *Oxyuranus*

COASTAL TAIPAN *Oxyuranus scutellatus*
INLAND TAIPAN *Oxyuranus microlepidotus*
WESTERN DESERT TAIPAN *Oxyuranus temporalis*

TAIPAN. THE NAME IS LEGENDARY. These snakes are hailed and feared as among the world's most lethal. All three species are large snakes, growing to more than 2m. They have narrow heads, large eyes and orange flecks on the belly. Scales are weakly glossed in 21–23 mid-body rows, the anal scale is single and the subcaudal scales are divided.

The western desert taipan was only discovered in late 2006 in the remote eastern interior of Western Australia. Very few specimens have been encountered and little is known of its lifestyle. There are no recorded bites but it is assumed to be highly dangerous. The two other species have been well studied.

Although they live in completely different habitats, the coastal and inland taipans share significant features regarding diet and venom. Most venomous snakes take a variety of vertebrate prey, but taipans are mammal specialists. They feed particularly on rats, which can easily retaliate. To deal with such potentially dangerous prey, taipans have developed a two-pronged attack strategy. They have extremely toxic venom (almost unrivalled among snakes) that's delivered with a unique 'strike-and-release' method. Essentially, a massive dose of venom is delivered via several fast bites, and the prey is released at minimal risk to the snake, with the certainty that it will be rapidly immobilised. The snake can then follow its victim and dine at leisure.

Taipans are egg-layers that produce large clutches of up to 22 eggs They are extremely shy and quick to vanish if approached. However, if provoked they can deliver a series of rapid strikes in quick succession. They have long fangs capable of deeply injecting large amounts of highly toxic venom.

Before antivenom was developed, a taipan bite was almost inevitably fatal. The bite site is usually relatively painless, although swelling and local tissue damage have been reported. Envenomation effects include severe paralysis, a marked deterioration in blood clotting, muscle destruction, a loss of consciousness and often renal failure. Symptoms may develop extremely rapidly. Clearly, no-one with an ounce of common sense would ever interfere with a taipan!

Inland taipan

COASTAL TAIPAN
Oxyuranus scutellatus
(Previous page)

The coastal taipan has a sleek copper–brown body and 'coffin-shaped' head with a cream snout and angular brows above large orange-brown eyes. It occurs in tropical to subtropical northern and eastern Australia and New Guinea, extending south to about Grafton, in New South Wales. Its core habitat seems to be woodlands with tall grasses.

This snake has adapted well to at least some human modification, such as Queensland's cane fields, which are also a favoured habitat.

To witness a large foraging coastal taipan is truly awe-inspiring. It has a majesty of movement, an attitude of supremacy and aura of intelligence that suggest a unique product of evolutionary success.

SNAKES

INLAND TAIPAN
Oxyuranus microlepidotus

The inland taipan has a black head and narrow oblique streaks on the body forming a herringbone pattern. Individuals change colour with the seasons, from pale yellow-brown in summer, darkening to a rich brown in winter. It's speculated that darker hues enhance their ability to absorb heat when basking early in the morning.

The inland taipan inhabits some of the harshest terrain in Australia – the arid Channel Country, which extends from south-western Queensland to the interior of South Australia. The featureless open shrublands, interspersed with dry channels, are subject to long, withering droughts followed by infrequent flood events.

The inland taipan's fortunes are closely pegged to those of its principal prey, the native Australian long-haired rat (*Rattus villosissimus*). Following heavy rains, the land responds with a flush of growth and the rats breed prolifically to reach plague proportions. They provide the inland taipans with a near-limitless glut of food, triggering the snakes to breed. Inevitably drought returns, rat numbers crash and lean times return for the snakes.

Western desert taipan

WESTERN DESERT TAIPAN
Oxyuranus temporalis

This taipan is coloured mostly pale brown or lighter, with a paler head and possibly darker edges on the scales to the rear of its body, creating a herringbone pattern. It is likely its colour darkens in cooler months. Based on the few specimens studied, it appears to be the smallest taipan species, reaching a length of about 1.7m.

This poorly known snake has been recorded from remote deserts in far eastern Western Australia, near the Northern Territory and South Australia borders. Its habitat varies from sandy flats with grevillea, mallee, eucalypts, diverse shrubs and spinifex to dunes and gravelly rises. There is also an old record from the NT's George Gill Ranges.

Preserved specimens and faecal samples indicate this species, like other taipans, has a specialised diet of small mammals.

Acanthophis praelongus

Northern death adder

DEATH ADDERS

GENUS *Acanthophis*

COMMON DEATH ADDER *Acanthophis antarcticus*
BARKLY TABLELAND DEATH ADDER *Acanthophis hawkei*
KIMBERLEY DEATH ADDER *Acanthophis lancasteri*
DESERT DEATH ADDER *Acanthophis pyrrhus*
NORTHERN DEATH ADDER *Acanthophis praelongus*
PAPUAN DEATH ADDER *Acanthophis rugosus*
PILBARA DEATH ADDER *Acanthophis wellsi*

THESE DISTINCTIVE SNAKES have a broad triangular head, short, thick body, and an abruptly thin tail with a segmented tip ending in a curved spur. Mid–body scales are in 19–23 rows, the anal scale is single, and subcaudal scales are single anteriorly and divided posteriorly. All species have a ragged banded pattern but colours, ranging from brown or grey to brick-red, vary according to species and the substrate on which they live.

Death adders are absent from Victoria but have a patchy distribution and abundance across all other mainland states. They give birth to live young, producing litters of up to 40 or more.

These snakes are ambush predators that rely on superb camouflage and sedentary habits to keep hidden and avoid danger – lying motionless, partly concealed in leaf litter or vegetation with the body in a loose coil and tail resting near the snout. At the approach of a frog, lizard, mammal or bird, the tail-tip is wriggled to mimic a worm or caterpillar, luring victims within range of a lightning-fast strike.

Death adders are unwilling to flee when approached and can, like waiting landmines, be accidentally trodden on. Because they are so secretive they are seldom encountered, even where they are known to be common. Bites are extremely rare but normally occur on the foot.

Death adders have long, deeply penetrating fangs and one of the highest venom yields of any Australian snake. The venom barely affects blood coagulation or damages tissue but is powerfully neurotoxic. Symptoms include a mild headache and occasionally vomiting, tenderness or pain in the lymph nodes, and paralysis. This may affect all voluntary muscles, but cardiac muscles appear unaffected.

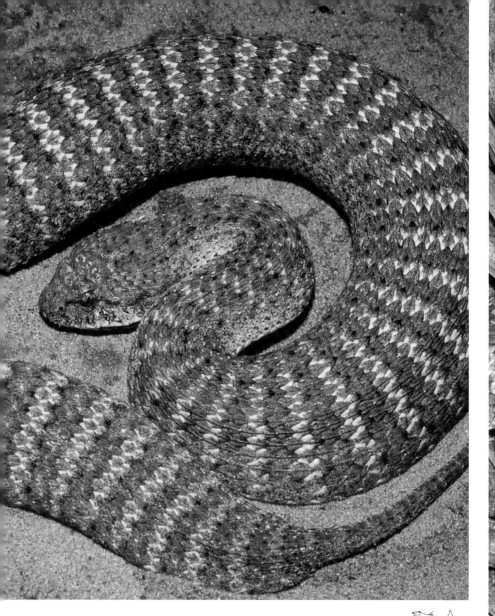

DESERT DEATH ADDER
Acanthophis pyrrhus

The desert death adder thrives in the vast spinifex deserts
of central and western Australia, but its distribution also
extends into arid habitats of all mainland states except New
South Wales and Victoria. The species occurs at its highest densities on
sand plains and rocky outcrops and it is often associated with spinifex.

This is one of the most strikingly marked death adders – usually
coloured red overall with distinctive lighter bands. It lures prey
(such as lizards, birds and frogs) by wiggling the thin tip of its tail,
mimicking a worm or lizard. Also like other death adders, this species'
venom is mostly neurotoxic.

COMMON DEATH ADDER
Acanthophis antarcticus

The common death adder is found in open forests, heaths and shrublands across much of eastern Australia and in a strip along the continent's southern margin in Western Australia and South Australia.

Adults usually prey on birds and small mammals, while juveniles are more inclined to take reptiles. This species' numbers, however, have declined significantly due to altered fire regimes and attempted predation on introduced cane toads. Colouration is either grey or reddish brown, with both forms occurring within most populations.

BROAD-HEADED SNAKES

GENUS *Hoplocephalus*

BROAD-HEADED SNAKE *Hoplocephalus bungaroides*
PALE-HEADED SNAKE *Hoplocephalus bitorquatus*
STEPHEN'S BANDED SNAKE *Hoplocephalus stephensii*

A S THE COMMON NAME suggests, these snakes are characterised by their wide, flattened head, clearly distinct from the neck. They also have barred lips; weakly glossed scales in 19–21 mid-body rows; an obvious notch on each side of the broad ventral scales; and single anal and subcaudal scales. They reach lengths of 80cm to just over 1m.

Australian venomous snakes are not usually good climbers, although all species occasionally turn up in trees or on rafters. But the broad-headed snakes are primarily arboreal and rock-inhabiting, so they are adept climbers. Distinctive notches on the ventral scales are associated with a long keel along each side of the belly. These are designed to grip on rough rock, bark or wood for the easy ascent of steep or vertical surfaces.

All three species feed on vertebrates, but each has different prey preferences. The broad-headed snake takes mainly lizards (particularly skinks and geckos), the pale-headed snake prefers frogs and the Stephen's banded snake feeds on lizards, frogs, mammals and birds. They produce live young with litters of up to 12.

Encounters with these snakes are rare because they are either scarce or live in restricted habitats. They are also extremely shy. Virtually all known bites result from handling snakes by reptile researchers or keepers. When provoked they raise their flattened head and hold their forebody in an S-shape. Bites treated with tiger snake antivenom, though symptoms can resemble the bite of a brown snake. There are no recorded human fatalities.

Hoplocephalus stephensii

Stephen's banded snake

BROAD-HEADED SNAKE
Hoplocephalus bungaroides

The broad-headed snake has an extremely restricted distribution on sandstone cliffs between Sydney and the Nowra area, New South Wales. During mild times of the year snakes rely on thin rock slabs resting on flat sandstone, but during summer they shift into adjacent tree hollows.

Unfortunately, the removal of rock for gardens plus the illegal capture of these snakes by enthusiasts has severely reduced the species' numbers and available habitat. As a result, it has been listed as endangered under NSW threatened species legislation.

PALE-HEADED SNAKE
Hoplocephalus bitorquatus

Compared with the other species in this genus, the pale-headed snake has a wide distribution, occurring from north-eastern New South Wales to central and northern Queensland. It lives mostly in dry forests, often near watercourses. It is an adept climber, and often shelters in tree hollows and under loose bark.

Like all broad-headed snakes, it hunts at night, preying mostly on frogs and lizards. Also as with the other broad-headed snakes, tiger snake antivenom is used for bites.

Highlands copperhead

COPPER-HEADS

GENUS *Austrelaps*

LOWLANDS COPPERHEAD *Austrelaps superbus*
HIGHLANDS COPPERHEAD *Austrelaps ramsayi*
DWARF (PYGMY) COPPERHEAD *Austrelaps labialis*

THE THREE COPPERHEAD species are thickset with grey to rust-brown bodies, often with a reddish flush along the lower flanks. Despite the name, the head is not noticeably copper-coloured. Patterning is usually weak, although some individuals have a band across the neck and occasionally a narrow dark vertebral line. The head is relatively narrow with dark and pale bars on the upper lip. Scales are smooth and slightly glossed. Mid-body scales are in 15 rows, with a slightly enlarged row adjacent to the belly. Anal and subcaudal scales are single.

Copperheads are mainly associated with marshy habitats and restricted to cool temperate southern Australia. Lowlands copperheads occur in southern Victoria and Tasmania; highlands copperheads occur in mountains from eastern Victoria to north-eastern New South Wales; and the dwarf copperhead is restricted to South Australia's Mt Lofty Ranges and Kangaroo Island. They feed on vertebrates, particularly frogs but also lizards, mammals and even fish. They are live-bearers, producing litters of up to 16 young.

Copperheads are usually placid snakes that slide from view if approached. They are reluctant to bite, even when provoked. Instead, they flatten the head and neck to form a weak hood, hiss loudly and may strike.

Bites from copperheads are poorly documented. The venom is similar to that of the tiger snake, so muscle destruction, paralysis, local pain and swelling are likely complications. A severe, untreated bite could certainly prove fatal.

HIGHLANDS COPPERHEAD
Austrelaps ramsayi

The highlands copperhead grows to slightly longer than 1m. The bars on the upper lips are broad and conspicuous. It is extremely cool-tolerant, extending from montane forests to herb fields high in the Australian Alps. Its dark colouration helps maximise the amount of heat it can absorb from the sun.

LOWLANDS COPPERHEAD
Austrelaps superbus

The lowlands copperhead is the largest species in this group, growing up to 1.2m across much of its range, and more than 1.5m on King Island in Bass Strait. The bars on the upper lips are narrow and often ill-defined. High densities occur at some suitable sites where, on a mild sunny morning, they can be observed hunting for frogs among waterside vegetation.

ROUGH-SCALED SNAKE

GENUS *Tropidechis*

Tropidechis carinatus

THE ROUGH-SCALED snake is the only member of its genus. It's named for the raised longitudinal keels – one per scale – aligned to form low parallel ridges along its back and sides. Keeled body scales are unusual among Australian snakes. The harmless keelback snake, *Tropidonophis mairii*, shares the condition, looks like the rough-scaled snake and also occurs in close proximity to it around eastern Australia, so there is potential for the venomous species to be confused with the non-venomous. Both snakes range in colour through shades of brown, olive to grey, usually with ragged dark bands or transverse blotches, and both grow to about 75cm.

But rough-scaled snakes differ in having a box-shaped head with parallel sides and a squared snout, straight mouth and plain upper lips. They have 23 mid-body scale rows and single anal and subcaudal scales. Keelbacks have a more rounded snout, up-curved mouth and dark vertical 'sutures' between upper-lip scales. The mid-body scales are in just 15 rows and

the anal and subcaudal scales are divided.

Rough-scaled snakes mostly occupy cool, moist areas in subtropical eastern Australia, from coastal northern New South Wales lowlands to southern Queensland. A northern population is isolated on mountains in Queensland's Wet Tropics. Most localities are high altitudes, while keelbacks prefer adjacent warmer lowlands, meaning the two species do not normally occur together.

Rough-scaled snakes can be active by day or night depending on temperature. Unlike most venomous Australian snakes, they are adept climbers. They feed on vertebrates, particularly frogs, mammals and lizards. They are live-bearers, with litters of up to 19 young.

The species can be aggresssive if provoked and will deliver one or two rapid strikes. The venom, which is similar to that of a tiger snake, affects peripheral nerves, causing paralysis, damage to muscle fibres and blood-clotting anomalies.

TIGER SNAKE

GENUS: *Notechis*

Notechis scutatus

THE TIGER SNAKE is named for the conspicuous banded pattern typical of the species on mainland Australia, although plain individuals are common. In the east they are rich brown to khaki with ragged paler bands. Those in the west are often black with yellow bands. In Tasmania, the islands of the Bass Strait and parts of South Australia, plain black forms predominate. There are multiple subspecies across Australia – all have broad heads, blunt, squared snouts and smooth scales. Mid-body scales are in 17–19 rows; and anal and subcaudal scales are all single. They are live-bearers, producing litters of up to 37.

Tiger snakes are mostly restricted to cool temperate southern Australia, where they favour moist habitats. Towards Queensland, their range becomes increasingly fragmented and restricted to upland areas.

They feed on vertebrates, and certain populations subsist on restricted diets, which has influenced the way they have evolved. On Bass Strait's Mount Chappell Island, for example, they depend on a seasonal glut of muttonbirds: the snakes gorge on chicks until they grow too large to swallow, then fast for the rest of the year. This has favoured the evolution of gigantism, with the island's largest tiger snakes reaching 2m. Meanwhile on SA's Roxby Island, small lizards are the only available prey and tiger snakes there barely exceed 60cm. On the mainland, with wider prey options, they reach just over 1m. Tiger snakes are common near densely populated areas and are among the most frequently encountered venomous snakes.

Exaggerated tales abound of their ferocity. Snakes may stand their ground, holding the fore-body in an oblique curve, flattening the head and neck and hissing loudly. It is an impressive display, but attacks are extremely rare.

Tiger snake venom can produce a range of severe effects. It has components that affect blood clotting and interfere with how nerves transmit and receive messages. Early symptoms include nausea, vomiting, headache followed by visual disturbances, paralysis, muscle destruction and kidney failure.

CLOSE CALL
When it comes to snakebites, Jo Sambono knows from personal experience about how fine the line between life and death can be.

1ST
PERSON

A dangerous obsession

A love for dangerous death adders almost cost **Joe Sambono** his life.

IN 1975 I WAS aged 19 and obsessed with snakes, particularly death adders, and determined to breed the dangerous species. I had a monster-sized female and felt sure she was pregnant.

One day I picked her up to inspect her and her swollen belly left me in no doubt. When I released her, I pulled my hand back quickly, but felt a long fang pierce my right index finger. Knowing I was in trouble, I applied a compression bandage to my arm and my friend Martin drove me to hospital, where I was admitted to the intensive care unit (ICU) at 6pm. After a test to confirm the venom type, I was given antivenom premedication and from here my memories are disjointed. I felt drowsy, which, the doctors explained, was the effect of the premedication. Then I began to feel really strange. I developed a headache, became thirsty, was soon barely able to open my eyes and felt weak all over. The doctors told me they were going to administer death adder antivenom, but I remember thinking I didn't care – I just wanted water. Mercifully, someone gave me

a sip. But the venom had affected my swallowing ability and I was quietly choking before a doctor worked out what was going on. Breathing difficulties followed, then I passed out and was put on a respirator at 8:30pm. I continued to deteriorate and eventually went into cardiac arrest due to a reaction to the antivenom premedication. I remained on a respirator overnight, and wasn't given more antivenom until 11am the next day. I had no further reaction, but didn't really start to recover until I received a third dose about an hour later. By the end of the day I was taken off life support and began to breathe for myself. Five days later, I was released and that should have been the end of the story.

Ten days later I was back in ICU, covered in welts and struggling to breathe. I had 'serum sickness': an allergic-like reaction to the horse-made antibodies in the antivenom. I left hospital the next day, although my finger took months to return to normal.

But when my death adder soon gave birth to 15 perfect offspring I knew my obsession with snakes was as strong as ever.

SNAKE SAFETY

Follow these simple rules to reduce the risk of snakebite when you're in the bush. And remember that if you *do* see a snake, be assured it will be as keen to avoid the encounter as you are. Stop, step back slowly and watch it go about its business.

- Never bushwalk alone: it's always better to have help at hand.

- **If you make some noise snakes are likely to feel the vibrations and move away, so stomp along and bang the ground with your walking poles.**

- Wear appropriate footwear, gaiters and clothing to reduce the amount of bare skin around your feet, ankles and lower legs.

- **Watch where you put your feet, and remember it's preferable to step onto an obstacle such as a log or rock than over it. That way you can see what's on the other side.**

- Be particularly careful when walking around watercourses; they're favourite places for snakes.

- **Always have a first aid kit at hand; make sure you know snakebite first aid (see pages 52–53) and have enough bandages with you.**

- Always tell someone where you're going, and when you expect to return.

- **If you find a snake near your home don't try to kill it or catch it. Call the local wildlife rescue group or state wildlife authority to request a snake-catcher.**

100   0

HIGHLY VENOMOUS   **LESS VENOMOUS**

1. Inland taipan

2. Eastern brown snake

3. Coastal taipan

4. Tiger snake

5. Tiger snake (black variety)

6. Beaked sea snake

MOST VENOMOUS

Australia is home to the **10 most venomous** snake species and subspecies in the world.

7. Western tiger snake

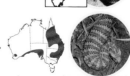

Chappell Island tiger snake

Common death adder

Western brown snake

Source: Toxicity index, Australian Venom Research Unit, University of Melbourne

FIRST ✚ AID

SNAKEBITE

WARNING
DO NOT wash venom off the skin
DO NOT cut the bitten area
DO NOT try to suck venom out of the wound
DO NOT use a tourniquet
DO NOT try to catch the snake

WHAT TO LOOK OUT FOR

Signs are not always visible but there may be puncture marks, bleeding or scratches.

Symptoms developing within an hour may include headache, impaired vision, nausea, vomiting, diarrhoea, breathing difficulties, drowsiness, fainting, problems speaking or swallowing.

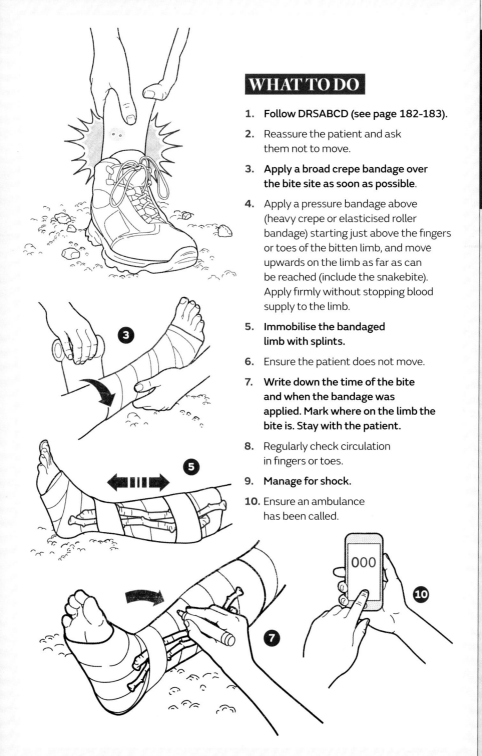

WHAT TO DO

1. Follow DRSABCD (see page 182-183).

2. Reassure the patient and ask them not to move.

3. **Apply a broad crepe bandage over the bite site as soon as possible.**

4. Apply a pressure bandage above (heavy crepe or elasticised roller bandage) starting just above the fingers or toes of the bitten limb, and move upwards on the limb as far as can be reached (include the snakebite). Apply firmly without stopping blood supply to the limb.

5. **Immobilise the bandaged limb with splints.**

6. Ensure the patient does not move.

7. **Write down the time of the bite and when the bandage was applied. Mark where on the limb the bite is. Stay with the patient.**

8. Regularly check circulation in fingers or toes.

9. **Manage for shock.**

10. Ensure an ambulance has been called.

Wolf spider

AUSTRALIA'S MOST DANGEROUS ARACHNIDS ARE MOSTLY SMALL, DARK AND INCONSPICUOUS CREATURES. BUT DON'T BE FOOLED! MANY CAN MAKE YOU VERY ILL AND A FEW ARE EVEN KILLERS.

SPIDERS
AND OTHER ARACHNIDS

THE INVERTEBRATE CLASS Arachnida includes 11 groups of eight-legged creatures, the best known of which are the spiders, scorpions, ticks and mites. The spiders – Araneae – are the most numerous, and perhaps most feared, group.

About 3300 spider species have so far been described in Australia, including 50 that may pose a danger to humans, although only a few have been implicated in serious envenomations. This hasn't prevented a general fear of spiders here and the reason for that may be that we have one of the world's deadliest – the Sydney funnel-web (see pages 56–61) – although no deaths have been attributed to this species since an antivenom was introduced in 1981.

In general, spiders do far more good than harm; their daily catch of flies and other irritating insects alone is cause enough for celebration. They're also wonderful animals to observe: a spider building its web is one of nature's best shows.

The other arachnids in this book – ticks and scorpions – seem to get similarly bad press. Our scorpions suffer undeservedly from association with deadly overseas relatives. Ticks are a different story. The paralysis tick is common throughout many of Australia's main population centres and can cause severe allergic reactions in some people. It also affects livestock and is the cause of many deaths among companion animals and thousands of veterinary treatments. We have also included the myriapods here, the many-legged centipedes and millipedes.

10 SPECIES
0 DEATHS

THERE ARE **10 SPECIES** OF SPIDER OF CONCERN BUT **0 DEATHS** SINCE ANTIVENOMS WERE DEVELOPED

FUNNEL-WEB SPIDERS

FAMILY Hexathelidae

SYDNEY FUNNEL-WEB *Atrax robustus*
BLUE MOUNTAINS FUNNEL-WEB *Hadronyche versuta*
NORTHERN TREE (NORTHERN RIVERS)
FUNNEL-WEB *Hadronyche formidabilis*
TOOWOOMBA FUNNEL-WEB *Hadronyche infensa*
VICTORIAN FUNNEL-WEB *Hadronyche modesta*

FUNNEL-WEBS BELONG to the ancient group of spiders known as mygalomorphs, which all have stout bodies and are mostly ground dwelling. Unlike the modern araneomorph spiders, their large fangs work up and down, instead of sideways.

Funnel-webs are nocturnal and most spend the daylight hours hidden away in silk-lined burrows with entrances obscured beneath logs, stones, tussocks or leaf litter.

At night during the warmer months, males wander about in search of females, making this the key danger period for people. Digging about in moist parts of the garden can uncover them during the day, and a disturbed funnel-web is very aggressive. Anyone who has seen one in its raised attack posture, holding its very long fangs high and ready for a strike, will not only use gardening gloves, but invest in even stouter ones!

Australia has at least 40 species of funnel-web including six reported to have caused severe envenomation in people. However, our knowledge of the true extent of all species called funnel-webs is in a state of flux. These spiders are mostly restricted to more temperate and humid areas of the east coast and ranges, from Tasmania to northern Queensland, although one species lives in South Australia's dry Eyre Peninsula.

The very fine features that distinguish one funnel-web species from another are not useful in the field. See the Sydney funnel-web entry (overleaf) for a description of this group, and treat all funnel-web-like spiders as being extremely dangerous.

Sydney funnel-web

BLUE MOUNTAINS FUNNEL-WEB
Hadronyche versuta

The Blue Mountains funnel-web shares its coastal range with the Sydney funnel-web, but also extends out to the drier range country as far west as the town of Orange. Females are up to 35mm long and their burrows tend to have a web-lined entrance hidden beneath logs. The amount of venom delivered in a strike is similar to that of the Sydney funnel-web. However, because of their very retiring habits, bites are rare. They can be succesfully treated with Sydney funnel-web antivenom. All species within the *Hadronyche* genus should be regarded as potentially very dangerous.

SYDNEY FUNNEL-WEB
Atrax robustus

The female Sydney funnel-web has a body about 35mm long, while the deadlier male is about 25mm. Both are black all over, making them identifiably different from the superficially similar mouse and trapdoor spiders, which usually have bodies of some other hues mixed with black or brown. However, because the finer points of identification can be difficult, it is safest to assume all similar spiders are this one, and are therefore best given a wide berth.

The Sydney funnel-web is recognised as one of the world's most deadly spiders (see page 68). The immediate effect of a bite is severe pain at the site, followed by profuse sweating, saliva production and muscle tremors, with the pain and cramps spreading to other parts of the body. Rapid first aid is essential (see pages 180–187) and the victim must have antivenom administered as soon as possible.

The Sydney funnel-web has two close relatives in the *Atrax* genus with a similar range but extending to south-eastern New South Wales and into the Snowy Mountains. The bite of these species is not as well documented but presumed to be potentially as dangerous.

Only some of the more than 30 funnel-web species in the genus *Hadronyche* have achieved the status of a common name. The northern tree funnel-web (*H. formidabilis*) is found in wet forests from the Hunter Valley, NSW, north to Queensland' south-east highlands.It is the largest known species, with females reaching 50mm in body length. Their shallow web-covered retreats are usually under the bark of rainforest trees, both as fallen logs and on standing trees up to 30m above ground. There are few recorded bites. Victims have presented with serious and painful symptoms leading to a semi-comatose state. Sydney funnel-web antivenom has been administered and has resulted in full recovery, but in some cases had to be given at a dose four times greater than normal. Other tree-dwelling funnel-webs are distributed over the wet forests of the east.

SYDNEY FUNNEL-WEB SPIDER ♀

Actual size

CM 0 1 2 3 4 5 6

SIZE MATTERS

The Sydney funnel-web female shown here has a body about 35mm long, while the smaller, deadlier male is about 25mm. The northern tree funnel-web (*H. formidabilis*) is the largest funnel-web species known so far, with females achieving body lengths of up to 50mm.

Sydney funnel-web

Funnel-webs have been known to survive up to 30 hours in water, trapped inside a small air bubble.

REDBACK SPIDER

Latrodectus hasselti

T HE FEMALE, WHICH is considerably larger
than the male of the species, is a shiny, smooth
black spider with an hourglass-shaped red
marking on her underside, and a red to orange stripe on
top. Her body is pea-shaped and about 10mm long
with thin black legs. Males are less than 5mm, lighter in
colour and simply too small to bite people.

Redbacks find human dwellings very attractive, and
have developed a long and fabled association with us.
Every house probably has some of their typically messy,
dense webs in corners and under overhangs.

The webs are usually at least as deep as wide, with the
female spider hiding out of view during the day.
Somewhere below the web are ingenious vertical,
sticky threads, which are held taut by a complex series
of 'guide rope' threads. When an insect walking past
gets entangled, the vertical lines snap and propel the
prey off the ground to where the spider can best subdue
it. Redbacks are among the *Latrodectus* species that
practise sexual cannibalism – the female consumes the
male after, or sometimes during, mating – hence the
group's common name of 'widow' spiders.

These spiders rarely leave their webs and are not
aggressive, but their constant presence near humans
means that several hundred people a year are bitten.
The initial bite apparently does not hurt, but the pain
and a burning sensation develop after about five
minutes. Reactions to their neurotoxic venom vary, but
sweating around the bite area, stiffness, nausea, muscle
weakness, chest pains and tremors are usual. Before the
antivenom was developed in 1956, 13 people were
known to have died from redback bites. No deaths have
been recorded since, but the redback's loss of reputation
as a killer does not signal that it's okay to be less vigilant
around them. Prompt first aid (see page 185) and proper
medical attention after a bite are essential, because most
victims still need the antivenom to avoid serious health
risks or even death.

Female redback spider

REDBACK ♀

Actual size

CM 0 1

The female redback's body, shown here, is about 1cm long excluding the legs. Males are smaller, about 4mm, but are rarely seen.

MOUSE SPIDERS

FAMILY Actinopodidae

EASTERN MOUSE SPIDER *Missulena bradleyi*
RED-HEADED MOUSE SPIDER *Missulena occatoria*
LESSER RED-HEADED MOUSE SPIDER *Missulena insignis*

THIS FAMILY OF SPIDERS belongs to the mygalomorph group of primitive ground-dwelling spiders, along with other trapdoor spiders and the funnel-webs. There are currently eight species in the genus in Australia. They are stout with a very broad head, very large downward acting fangs, and relatively short legs. Body length varies from about 15 to 25mm. The most apparent difference from funnel-webs lies in the head, which is broader, raised at the front and has its eight eyes spread along the entire width on top. Funnel-webs and other mygalomorphs have the eyes grouped in the centre of the top of the head.

Mouse spiders vary in colour. They can be brown, grey to black, and red-headed mouse spider males have a spectacular combination of a bright red head and blue abdomen.

Mouse spiders tend to live in burrows with a well-disguised, hinged lid. The females spend most of their lives in or near the burrow, but the males rarely dig in, and wander around in the warmer months looking for females. Unlike funnel-webs, red-headed mouse spiders may do this in daylight.

Little is known of the venom of this group, but it has been shown to be chemically very similar to that of the funnel-webs. A study on the female of the red-headed species showed a capacity to kill baby mice even quicker than a funnel-web. Luckily, it's very rare to encounter the burrow-bound females.

A bite from a male of the eastern mouse species is the only confirmed envenomation for this group. A 19-month-old girl was bitten in southern Queensland and went into a coma. She was given funnel-web antivenom – because there is no mouse spider antivenom – and recovered fully. Mouse spiders are not as aggressive as funnel-webs, and so bites are rare, and sometimes 'dry' (venomless), but they should be treated with the same caution as funnel-webs.

Red-headed mouse spider

Missulena occatoria

SPIDERS

EASTERN MOUSE ♂

Actual size

CM 0   1   2   3

The male eastern mouse spider shown here has a body length of about 1.5cm. Females are larger, up to 3cm in body length.

WOLF SPIDER ♂

Actual size

CM 0 1 2 3

Female wolf spiders carry their young spiderlings on their back, even when in their burrow.

Lycosa godeffroyi

WOLF SPIDERS

FAMILY Lycosidae

Lycosa godeffroyi and other species
Other common names: garden wolfs, Union Jack spiders

THESE STOUT-BODIED, grey to brown, ground-dwelling spider species vary in body size from about 1 to 8cm. The front half – the carapace – is raised and often has markings radiating from the centre, which has led to some being called 'Union Jack' spiders.

The eyes are the most most definitive feature of wolf spiders. Other ground-dwelling spiders tend to have their eight eyes in a tight group on top of the carapace. On a wolf spider's raised carapace the eyes are set in the vertical surface, looking straight ahead. Two of them are very noticeable, being larger than in any other ground-dwelling spiders.

Wolf spiders are efficient hunters and their large eyes are an advantage on night hunts to find and run down their mainly insect prey. These spiders are common in most landscapes. Go out with a headtorch at night with the beam aligned with the direction of your eyes. As you scan the ground you will notice very bright and sometimes colourful pinpoints of light reflecting the torchlight: most of these will belong to the largest eyes of wolf spiders.

Wolf spiders are not especially aggressive and usually hide in their shallow burrows by day. The danger is when you're working in the garden and may dig one up and accidentally provoke a bite – a good reason to wear gardening gloves. The bite is very painful, but the rest of the symptoms vary widely. Some people will get a rapid pulse, nausea and even dizziness. Kidney damage has been reported.

In the longer term, this spider has been linked with bacterial infections. Many potentially dangerous bacteria live in the soil, and these spiders share this habitat, so may pick up and inject bacteria under the skin when they bite.

There is some controversy about the dangers of wolf spiders because people very rarely catch the culprit to definitively link the spider with the symptoms. However, while human reactions are generally not dangerous, dogs and cats can die from their bite.

SPIDERS

THE WORLD'S DEADLIEST SPIDERS

Dangerous rivalry

Brazilian wandering spiders (*Phoneutria* spp.) and the Sydney funnel-web (*Atrax robustus*) are usually cited as the world's most dangerous spiders to humans. Both have highly toxic venom and, compared with other spiders, typically have longer fangs and inject more venom when they strike.

There is an added issue with funnel-web venom: its key ingredient is a toxic nerve-affecting protein called atraxotoxin, which is delivered in much higher doses by the males.

The presence of atraxotoxin is an evolutionary mystery. Most native Australian animals are not affected by it, but the nervous system of primates (including humans) is, despite not having

VENOM CALL
To maintain a Sydney funnel-web venom supply for antivenom production, the Sydney Reptile Park asks the public to bring spiders to collection points, such as hospitals. The response (above) can sometimes be overwhelming!

shared the funnel-web's habitat during much of the spider's evolution.

This quirk made early work on funnel-web antivenom very difficult because of the lack of suitable test animals. It took nearly 30 years to produce the final working version of the antivenom, which has been saving lives since the early 1980s.

At least 13 deaths had been attributed to Sydney funnel-web bites since 1927, when the first victim was identified.

Brazilian wandering spider

WHITE-TAILED ♂

CM 0   1   2

Lampona cylindrata

WHITE-TAILED SPIDERS

GENUS *Lampona*
Lampona cylindrata, Lampona murina

WHITE-TAILS HAVE elongate cylindrical bodies about 20mm long. They're dark with reddish-coloured legs, a whitish tip to the abdomen and sometimes two or four other lighter spots on the flanks.

They are roving hunters, only building small sac-like webs for hiding, not prey capture. They mainly feed on other spiders, which they often lure close by imitating the vibrations of an insect caught in their webs. Outdoors, they live under bark and logs and hunt at night. But they can move into houses and are often seen wandering on floors and walls during the night, particularly in summer.

Their bite causes local, sometimes severe, pain. Symptoms can include headache, nausea and skin lesions. Because white-tails are so common, they are blamed for many indoor bites, even when the specimen is not seen or caught to prove the link. White-tails have also attracted attention because of a presumed association between their bite and necrotic (ulcerating skin lesion) effects. Because spiders feed on a liquid diet, they inject a flesh-dissolving enzyme during or after their bite. In most cases this causes only minor blistering and local cell death. But in some rare but dramatic cases, a severe allergic blistering or ulceration of the skin, similar to gangrene, has been reported. Some experts believe, but have yet to prove, that this may not be caused directly by the spider but by the necrotic bacterium *Mycobacterium ulcerans* entering the skin during the bite. It's also possible the bacterium gets into the puncture wound after the event, because it's freely present in the environment, especially in soil.

YOU'RE MORE LIKELY TO DIE FROM...

A USTRALIA'S REPUTATION as a danger zone for all things that bite and sting continues to grow among visitors from abroad – and to mystify locals. The website *VirtualTourist* lists 1737 tips on warnings and dangers for Australia; New Zealand draws a paltry 438 tips. Surely it's not all that bad?

Of course it isn't. Deaths caused by accident or misadventure are no bigger blips on the Australian mortality radar than they are on that of most developed countries. Here, you're exponentially more likely to die in a road collision, by drowning or by 'poisoning' – a category that includes deaths from narcotics, alcohol and accidental poisoning from prescribed medicines. Annual deaths from shark attack and snakebite are statistically so minor they barely register.

In contrast, the World Health Organization's (WHO) Animal Bites Fact Sheet No 373 (February 2013) estimated that there are annually 94,000–125,000 fatal snakebites worldwide, the vast majority in poor rural areas in Africa and South-East Asia where residents have poor access to health care and antivenoms.

The world's most deadly animal to humans – the mosquito – and the parasites and diseases it spreads are also of considerably less concern in Australia. WHO estimates that there were 212 million cases of malaria worldwide in 2015, and 429,000 deaths, more than 390,000 of them in the African region. In 2013–14, Australian health authorities reported only 373 cases of malaria, all of them acquired overseas.

For more mosquito information see page 92.

For more mosquito information see page 92.

THE TERRIBLE TOLL OF **MALARIA**

Malaria is still a major cause of death worldwide, particularly in Sub-Saharan Africa.

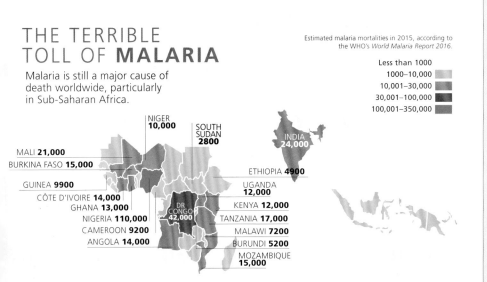

Estimated malaria mortalities in 2015, according to the WHO's *World Malaria Report 2016*.

Less than 1000
1000–10,000
10,001–30,000
30,001–100,000
100,001–350,000

NIGER **10,000**
SOUTH SUDAN **2800**
INDIA **24,000**
MALI **21,000**
BURKINA FASO **15,000**
ETHIOPIA **4900**
GUINEA **9900**
UGANDA **12,000**
CÔTE D'IVOIRE **14,000**
GHANA **13,000**
KENYA **12,000**
NIGERIA **110,000**
DR CONGO **42,000**
TANZANIA **17,000**
CAMEROON **9200**
MALAWI **7200**
ANGOLA **14,000**
BURUNDI **5200**
MOZAMBIQUE **15,000**

SPIDERS

Badumna insignis

BLACK HOUSE SPIDERS

GENUS *Badumna*

LARGE BLACK HOUSE SPIDER
Badumna insignis
SMALL BLACK HOUSE SPIDER
Badumna longinqua

THE BLACK HOUSE spiders are also commonly known as window spiders, due to their habit of building along windowsills. Each white, lacy and messy web hides a stout, almost black, velvety textured spider, about 15mm long. The abdomen has a fine mottled pattern composed of lighter hairs.

Webs often have a funnel-shaped section in which the spiders hide by day. As well as windows, these spiders may build webs under eaves, gutters, in brickwork and outside among rocks and bark. They are very shy, so bites are uncommon, but memorable.

The larger species, *Badumna insignis*, has more venom and is responsible for more recorded bites. Symptoms include severe pain, nausea, vomiting, perspiring, headaches and giddiness. But these effects are not usually long-lasting and recovery is complete.

Recent attention given to the house and white-tailed spiders (see page 70) as a result of reports of necrotic effects remain unproven but are not thought to be caused directly by their venom.

LARGE BLACK HOUSE ♀

CM   0   1   2

SPIDERS

With typically messy webs and dark hairy bodies, large black house spiders fit the scary arachnid image popular in fairy stories.

FIRST ✚ AID

SPIDER BITE

SIGNS & SYMPTOMS
General symptoms
Sharp pain at bite site
Profuse sweating
Nausea, vomiting and abdominal pain

Additional symptoms of a funnel-web spider bite

- copious secretion of saliva
- muscular twitching and breathing difficulty
- small hairs stand on end
- numbness around mouth
- copious tears
- disorientation
- fast pulse
- markedly increased blood pressure
- confusion leading to unconsciousness

- patchy sweating
- headache
- muscle weakness or spasms

Additional symptoms of a redback spider bite

- intense local pain that increases and spreads
- small hairs stand on end

Possible signs and symptoms of other spider bites

- burning sensation
- swelling
- blistering

WHAT TO DO

1. Follow DRSABCD (see pages 182–183). 2. Lie the patient down.
3. Calm and reassure the patient.

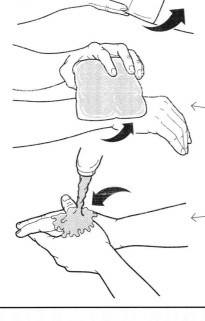

APPLY MANAGEMENT FOR:

FUNNEL-WEB/MOUSE SPIDER

- If on a limb, apply a broad crepe bandage over the bite site as soon as possible.

- **Apply a heavy crepe or elasticised roller bandage starting just above the fingers or toes of the bitten limb, and move upwards on the limb as far as can be reached (include the bite); apply firmly without stopping blood supply to the limb.**

- Immobilise the injured limb with splints and ensure the patient does not move.

- **Ensure an ambulance has been called.**

REDBACK SPIDER

- Apply an icepack (cold compress) to the bitten area to lessen pain.

- **Seek medical attention if patient develops severe symptoms.**

OTHER SPIDER BITES

- Wash with soap and water.

- **Apply icepack (cold compress) to relieve the pain.**

- Seek medical attention if patient develops severe symptoms.

SCORPIONS AND CENTIPEDES

Urodacus yaschenkoi

ORDER Scorpionida

MARBLED SCORPION *Lychas marmoreus*
BLACK ROCK SCORPION *Urodacus manicatus*
DESERT SCORPION *Urodacus yaschenkoi*
WOOD (FOREST) SCORPION *Cercophonius squama*

CLASS Chilopoda
AUSTRALIAN GIANT CENTIPEDE *Ethmostigmus rubripes*

Desert scorpion

WITH AN eight-legged body, including large pincers at the front and a barbed tail at the back, scorpions cannot be confused with anything else.

Centipedes, however, are sometimes confused with millipedes. Centipedes are flattened, have one pair of legs on the side of each body segment and large, modified front legs used as sideways-acting fangs, located behind the head. The harmless millipedes are largely cylindrical, have two pairs of legs under each body segment and no visible fangs.

All scorpions have a venomous sting and in other parts of the world, especially the tropics of the Americas and Africa, these arachnids are responsible for many deaths. Most Australian species, however, are known to have weak venom and there have been no confirmed deaths.

They should, nevertheless, be treated with respect and their bites avoided. It's common for there to be local pain for at least several hours and swelling for up to a few days after being bitten. Nausea has also been reported. Effort has not been put into developing antivenoms for Australian scorpion species because their venom is not considered dangerous enough. The recommended first aid is to apply an icepack to the sting site and seek medical help if pain persists.

Fast-scurrying centipedes have not been blamed for any deaths in Australia either. But they are famed for their bite, which produces sudden and very memorable pain. The larger they are, the more venom may enter a wound. The largest individuals recorded for the Australian giant centipede, our biggest species, have been up to 18cm in length.

Although unrelated, both scorpions and centipedes are nocturnal and hide in burrows and under stones, logs and bark by day. 'Something nasty in the woodpile' is an apt description for both groups.

Scorpions tend to be shy and bite only when accidentally cornered or stepped on. Centipedes, however, can react very aggressively to being disturbed. Note the centipede's many claw-tipped legs make this normally ground-dwelling creature a quick climber. Many people have learnt that one way to get bitten is to attack a centipede with a stick.

Australian giant centipede

Ethmostigmus rubripes

Ranging in colour from dark blue to orange-yellow, Australian giant centipedes like this one occur across the mainland, but not in Tasmania.

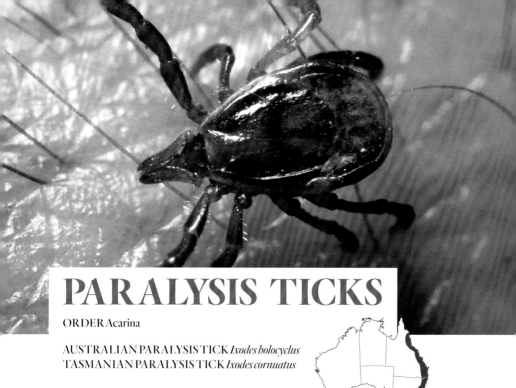

PARALYSIS TICKS

ORDER Acarina

AUSTRALIAN PARALYSIS TICK *Ixodes holocyclus*
TASMANIAN PARALYSIS TICK *Ixodes cornuatus*

Ixodes holocyclus

THOUSANDS OF domestic animals die each year from paralysis tick venom. Ticks are native species and feed on native mammals, which develop immunity to them.

The three stages in a tick's life cycle each require a blood meal. The 1mm-long, six-legged larvae, often called 'seed' or 'grass' ticks, are best known from the itch and occasional allergic symptoms they cause. They feed for up to six days; drop off and moult into match-head-sized, eight-legged nymphs; take another blood meal for up to eight days; then drop off and moult into adults. Adult females, which require a blood meal about 10 days before laying, are 3mm before feeding. They swell up to 400 per cent when feeding, then drop off and over several weeks scatter huge numbers of eggs on vegetation; then the cycle continues.

Many people have an allergic reaction to tick bites, notice the itching and swelling early and find and remove the tick. After many bites, these reactions can become severe and swelling around the neck can lead to serious breathing difficulties. Antihistamine drugs and an asthma inhaler can help in these cases.

The paralysis toxin tends not to seriously affect adults, but children are at risk. Early symptoms of weakness, anxiety and diarrhoea could indicate a tick. Paralysis can begin in the limbs in about five days. Removal of the tick is essential and follow-up medical attention critical. An antitoxin developed for dogs works, but can have unpleasant side effects in people, so it's a treatment of last resort. Most human patients recover without it.

When removing a tick it's important not to squeeze the tick's body, because more toxins may be injected. Daubing the tick with insect repellent or a pyrethrum-based spray may cause it to fall off.

Fine tweezers can be used to carefully grab the barbed feeding tube and pull it and the tick out together. Special tweezers designed not to squeeze the tick's body are available from chemists. Prevention is best: if you're spending time in the bush in known tick areas, check yourselves and your pets. Most insect repellents work on ticks and are advised, especially if you are prone to allergic reactions.

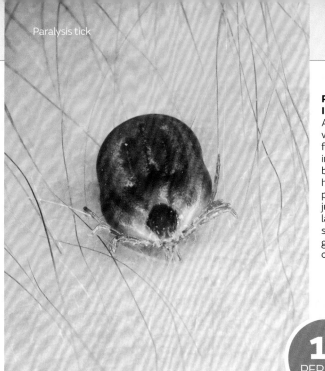

Paralysis tick

PARASITES IN WAITING
Adult female ticks wait in vegetation for vertebrates, including bushwalking humans, to brush past. They'll then jump on board and latch on to the skin where they gorge themselves on blood.

1ST PERSON

Checking for ticks

Robin Cruse has learnt to live with ticks by remaining vigilant and keeping antihistamines handy.

'VE LIVED in Kuranda, west of Cairns, Queensland, since the mid-1980s and have had three tick bites during that time. The first, which was not long after we moved here, produced the strongest reaction.

I noticed the tick about 7am, so I'd had it at least overnight. It was at the base of my skull and an itchy feeling alerted me to it. My husband pulled it out, but then, thinking that was it, drove off to Cairns, after which I became quite itchy all over. I went to have a shower and realised that my face was starting to swell up – my eyes had narrowed to little slits and I watched the red creep from under my armpits down my arms to my wrists, then down my body.

I got into the shower but became quite dizzy, and I thought, "I have to get up to the doctor's." So I exited the shower, got dressed and managed the short walk up into town. It was only 7:30am and the

doctor wasn't at work, so I went to a coffee shop where the owners, whom I knew, said: "Wow, what happened to you?" I was bright red, swollen, and slightly delirious. Luckily the doctor came in early so I toddled over to the surgery. He pumped me full of antihistamines, then drove me home and I went to sleep for the rest of the day. When I woke up I was mostly back to normal but I stayed sort of dopey and out of it for probably another day.

I had a similar, but not as severe, reaction – no face swelling – to one of the other tick bites I've had here. It was in 2007 and this bite made my throat swell up to the degree that I had a bit of trouble breathing. But the doctor gave me an intramuscular cortisone injection, which sorted it out quickly. The last bite I received, in 2014, really didn't create a reaction, although I did have an antihistamine on me, which I took as soon as I'd got the tick out.

BIGGEST DANGERS ON AUSTRALIAN LAND

THE ANIMALS on this list were distilled from *The top 30 dangerous animals in Australia*, first published on *australiangeographic.com.au*.

The top 30 list was compiled by staff of the Australian Museum, Sydney, who rated dangerous animals out of 10 based on the various facts, including the threat they pose to humans and the likelihood of encountering one in day-to-day life. See also *Top ten most dangerous marine creatures on page 159*.

DANGER RATING: (OUT OF 10)

Less dangerous, less likely to encounter

5

6

7

8

9

More dangerous, more likely to encounter

8

SYDNEY FUNNEL-WEB SPIDER
(*Atrax robustus*)

This is one of the world's most dangerous spiders. Its toxic venom evolved as a defensive tool against predators, rather than for attack. Unfortunately, humans are especially sensitive.

5

AUSTRALIAN PARALYSIS TICK
(*Ixodes holocyclus*)

Ticks rely on passing animals and humans to both feed and carry them.

7

BULL ANT
(*Myrmecia* spp.)

Some of the smaller species of this ant are known as jumper ants because of their habit of jumping towards any intruder. There are 90 known species in Australia.

5

RED-BELLIED BLACK SNAKE
(*Pseudechis porphyriacus*)

This placid city dweller can deliver a very nasty bite, but prefers to avoid human contact.

BIGGEST DANGER

HONEY BEE
(*Apis mellifera*)

9

Bees don't have particularly potent venom, but the allergic reaction suffered by 1–2 per cent of the population coupled with the high incidence of stings makes them second only to snakes as the most deadly venomous animals in Australia.

EASTERN BROWN SNAKE
(*Pseudonaja textilis*)

Despite more than 3000 cases of snakebite in Australia, there are usually just 2–3 fatalities. Most of those deaths are from the exceptionally toxic venom of the widely distributed eastern brown snake.

8

6

INLAND TAIPAN (*Oxyuranus microlepidotus*)

A potent mix of killer compounds makes this the world's most venomous snake, but they inhabit an isolated part of the country, so encounters are, thankfully, rare.

6

REDBACK SPIDER
(*Lactrodectus hasselti*)

No deaths have been recorded since the introduction of antivenom in the 1950s.

TIGER SNAKE
(*Notechis scutatus*)

Responsible for an average one death per year.

7

GIANT CENTIPEDE
(*Ethmostigmus rubripes*)

5

This 16cm nocturnal creature can cause severe pain but no deaths have been recorded in Australia.

A jumper ant attacking a bee

THEY MIGHT NOT LOOK AS SCARY AS AUSTRALIA'S
DEADLY REPTILES, SPIDERS AND SHARKS – BUT MANY
OF OUR INSECTS ALSO DESERVE TO BE AVOIDED.

INSECTS

IF SHEER WEIGHT of numbers is the measure, insects are the most successful type of organism on the planet. More than a million types of these six-legged invertebrates have been described, and estimates of the total number of species range up to 10 million. It's thought that insects might account for up to 90 per cent of all animal types on Earth.

Fortunately, most insects are beneficial to humans, or, at worst, little more than annoying. But there are a few that have well-deserved reputations as killers. With mosquitoes, for example, it's believed that a handful of species of these blood-suckers have been implicated in the deaths of up to half of all the humans who have ever lived.

Most of Australia's types of biting and stinging insects are familiar to all humanity: wasps, bees, ants and, of course, mosquitoes, which in Australia are associated with the spread of diseases such as dengue and Ross River fevers.

Some insects cause concern at the larval stage: a few types of moth caterpillars use poisonous hairs or venomous spines for self-defence, and while the effect on humans is usually little more than irritation or mild pain, some people can suffer severe allergic reactions.

2/100
ALLERGIC TO
BEE STINGS

BEE VENOM CAN CAUSE A LIFE-THREATENING ALLERGIC
REACTION IN APPROXIMATELY **2%** OF THE POPULATION

Apis mellifera

European honey bee

BEES

FAMILY Apidae

EUROPEAN HONEY BEE *Apis mellifera*

ASK HALF-A-DOZEN Australians to nominate the country's deadliest creatures and they'll probably rattle off an impressive catalogue of snakes, spiders and sharks with frightening capabilities to kill humans. The blue-ringed octopus, stonefish and box jellyfish are also likely to get a look in. But who'd expect to see the European honey bee on the list?

And yet this diligent little insect – first brought here in 1822 – kills one or two Australians a year. On average, sharks annually claim fewer lives and the national tally of deaths from spider bites is also lower.

For most of us, a bee sting causes only localised pain and swelling. The insects produce venom, called apitoxin, in abdominal glands and store it in special sacs. Although the toxin is poisonous to humans, each sting injects no more than 0.1mg. It's estimated it would take at least 500 jabs to kill the average adult human and this has never been known to occur in Australia. However, about 2 per cent of the population is thought to be allergic to honey bee venom. Within minutes of being stung, allergic individuals will develop symptoms of anaphylactic shock, during which airways can be obstructed and blood pressure plummets. They will usually require immediate medical attention. Immunotherapy treatment is also available, which slowly brings this immune system overreaction back to safer levels in the longer term.

Honey bees have a barbed sting that attaches so securely it rips from and kills the bee when it flies off, leaving the venom sac and barb. It's important not to remove the barb by squeezing it with your fingers, because this pumps in more venom. Unless you have fine tweezers by which to grasp the barb, use a scratching sideways motion to dislodge it.

BULL ANTS

GENUS *Myrmecia*

THIS ALMOST EXCLUSIVELY Australian genus includes about 90 species. Some that are of most concern to humans are also commonly known as jumper ants, jack-jumpers or sergeant ants. These ants are initially identified by their large size. The body of a foraging worker is 15–30mm long, with a pronounced elongated waist and very large, toothed mandibles, or jaws, which can be twice as long as the head.

Bull ant nests are mostly deep, underground galleries, sometimes with a volcano-like mound of excavated dirt around the entrance. Despite their huge jaws, the adults, as for all ants, eat only liquid food. Hapless insect victims carried into nests are for the white grub-like ant larvae, which devour at least some of their food as solids.

The workers are very aggressive, and attack any intruders approaching their large mound nests. Jumping species have a very skittish walk and can suddenly leap up to a height of 20cm. Their large, strong jaws are fearsome enough, but are not the real problem. They are designed to latch on to a victim so that the ant can then curve its abdomen forward to use its short, needle-like sting.

Ants are essentially wingless wasps and many have these stings as a method of defence. Unlike bees, whose sting has backward-pointing barbs, ant stings are very smooth and so fully retract after a jab. It is the venom injected via the sting that causes the sudden sharp pain, not the biting jaws. The venom itself is not a dangerous toxin, and usually results only in local pain and swelling. However, like many wasp venoms it can result in allergic reactions, especially after repeated bites, which can be serious and even life-threatening.

REAR-END ASSAULTS
Bull ants are found throughout Australia. Their venom, which is injected via a sting carried at the end of their rear segment, is not a dangerous toxin, but some people have a life-threatening allergy to it.

1ST PERSON

Ant attack!

They might be small but, as **Robin Anscomb** learnt the hard way, these organised insects should be taken very seriously.

OUR BLOCK AT Billen Cliffs, in northern New South Wales, had once been a beautiful garden, carefully planted by a previous owner. But, untended for 12 years, it had become overgrown with lantana, morning glory, cats paw, Crofton weed and mistflower.

While trying to clear it, I was stung by jumper ants on three or four occasions, each time resulting in memorable pain and a dedication to thicker clothes. Their nests were near old, rotted-out stumps or at the base of wattles. While pulling out Crofton weed one day I failed to notice a nest, and managed to pull three or four ants onto my thick, long-sleeved overalls. I brushed them off but not before being stung twice through the material. They were middle-sized ants and I knew I had to get back to the house and sit calmly before the pain struck. I failed.

My partner at that time tells me I turned red all over and was shouting incoherently, tearing off my clothes, retching white froth, and tearing my hair out in clumps. Antihistamines had no noticeable effect.

After many hours the pain eventually subsided, but many welts came up on my arm. All this from two stings.

I've remained truly scared of jumper ants since. They seem intelligent and organised. On a previous occasion I was going to chop down a black wattle in an inconvenient spot. I hit the base of the tree just once with the axe and large jumper ants swarmed up the trunk, lining themselves strategically along the lower lateral branches like an army. Others approached my legs along the ground. I retreated and the wattle remains. I've compared my experiences with other victims, and they've all agreed that these ants are definitely a special case.

There's no obvious communication as seen with other ants – like running around, touching each other – but I swear those on the wattle branches that day were looking right at me, waiting for me to get close enough to jump onto me.

When those aggresive jumper ants look at you they appear to make eye contact, which makes them scary little buggers by anybody's standard.

Cup moth caterpillar

STINGING CATERPILLARS

FAMILIES Several moth families,
but particularly *Limacodidae*

Other common names: Chinese junk,
spitfire, slug caterpillar

MANY CATERPILLARS have warning colouration, which indicates to predators, such as birds, that they have stored poisonous chemicals in their bodies from the plants they eat. This is not a problem for people, who usually don't eat them. But another caterpillar survival strategy – non-detaching, venom-producing spines – can be an issue. Caterpillars with such spines are described as urticating (irritating).

The cup moth caterpillars are particularly famous for their spines, as well as for their extraordinary appearance, the source of names such as slug caterpillar and Chinese junk.

They are brightly coloured in greens, yellows and reds, and their skin is smooth and snail-like. They also have short spines across the body that are either scattered or in clusters, looking somewhat like sea anemones. A sting from these hairs can be very painful and produce a weal reaction.

The most common species are 2–3cm long and live on eucalypt leaves in many parts of Australia. Brushing against them, or grabbing the leaf on which they're feeding, can cause the spines to break off and release their irritating fluids. The result is a very penetrating stabbing or burning type of pain, along with weals, which take many hours to calm down.

For first aid treatment see page 185.

Hairy Mary
caterpillar

HAIRY CATERPILLARS

FAMILIES Many families of moth, including the *Anthelidae, Lymantriidae, Nolidae* and *Notodontidae*

Other common names: tussock moth caterpillar, processionary caterpillar, Hairy Mary, and more

HUNDREDS of species of moth caterpillars are covered in hair. Not all are dangerous or even irritating to the touch, but a few can be a real problem – those that have non-envenomating hair with barbs or dart-ends that cause a mechanical irritation.

The worst of it is that symptoms can sometimes present even without contact with a caterpillar – the hairs are fragile and can easily be blown off. Species such as the browntail moth and the processionary caterpillars are communal, and large numbers shed their hair. The gumleaf skeletoniser caterpillar is not communal, luckily, because its hairs are potentially the worst. Once wind-borne, hairs can contact humans directly, or blow onto clothes on a drying line. They're so fine they can penetrate clothing fabric and eventually make their irritating skin-contact. Touching old cocoons left in the garden by caterpillars after they have metamorphosed can have the same effect.

Skin effects are generally minor, including stinging, rashes, pimples, itching and wheals, which may last for days. One type of hair causes allergic skin dermatitis that can be quite debilitating, and if hairs contact the eyes, the irritation can be very dangerous and medical help is advised.

For first aid treatment see page 185.

89

PAPER WASPS

Polistes humilis

CLASSIFICATION Paper wasps belong to *Polistinae*, a subfamily of the wasp family *Vespidae*. *Ropalidia* and *Polistes* are the main native genera; introduced species belong to the genus *Vespula*.

PAPER WASPS are colonial insects. Most species have bodies patterned in yellow and black warning colours, with a visible waist and pointy back end. Usually about 8–10mm long, they live in nests made of paper-like layers of hexagonal incubation cells. The 'paper' is a mix of weathered wood and wasp saliva that's fashioned into shape by the insect's jaws. Each cell contains an egg or developing larvae, which are fed on caterpillars hunted by the wasps. The nest structure varies with species, from a simple two cells under a leaf, to huge spirals enclosing many layers of cells in an outer, football-shaped, paper cover.

Paper wasps have small, sharp barb-less stings that can be used repeatedly. They are not aggressive while foraging, but if you wander near to, or disturb, a nest, a swarm may emerge and pursue you to inflict many stings. Most nests are in the bush, suspended under leaves, or in tree canopies. Closer to home some species suspend nests from wire fences, and others build under the eaves of houses. These home nests can present a real problem, especially if someone is allergic to the sting – people who know they are allergic to bee stings need to be especially careful. For most people the sting produces immediate sharp pain, and the sting site can be itchy or swollen for days afterwards.

For first aid treatment see page 185.

POTENTIAL KILLERS
Paper wasps can be beneficial garden insects. But people with allergic reactions to their venom need to be very careful around them. At least seven people in Australia are known to have been killed by allergic reactions to the stings of these insects

1ST PERSON

Paper-wasp hell

Robin Anscomb was shocked by her severe allergic reaction to a paper-wasp sting.

IN 1985 I BOUGHT a bare one-acre block near Kuranda, Queensland. On a late spring, not-too-hot morning, I began to mow the long grass and noticed a small paper-wasp nest hanging from the barbed wire fence. I was determined to avoid it at all costs because I'd been told of the painful sting, but not personally experienced it. Inevitably, however, I banged the nearest fencepost with the mower and disturbed them.

I moved to the block's other end to avoid them but was stung on the left hand, just once, between the little- and ring-finger joints. It hurt but not much, so I continued mowing, but with more vigour as a distraction. The distraction failed and the pain intensified.

I began sweating profusely and took off my shirt. Then I became disoriented, quite dizzy and found it increasingly difficult to breathe. I began to worry and thought that while I was able, I should drive to the doctor – the block was about 5km out of town. I started towards the car but fell over and really got worried when I began passing in and out of semi-consciousness. I couldn't cry out because my throat was swelling. And even if I'd been able to, the block was isolated and no-one would have heard me. Then I began to really lose consciousness. It became so difficult to breathe that I got scared.

As an educated, rational person, I knew that even if I made it to the car I wouldn't be able drive. However, my sharp pocket knife was in the car and I thought I could stick it in my throat as I'd seen on television, and open an airway. Even though the chance that I would kill myself was high, it seemed a better option than just succumbing...

Then I woke up. It was late afternoon. I was severely sunburnt with an intense headache, but otherwise well. I went carefully home, put myself to bed and slept for 24 hours.

The sunburn peeled and repaired, but I remain very anxious about paper wasps.

MOSQUITOES

CLASSIFICATION Family
Culicidae, which includes the
species of several genera that
can carry dangerous diseases
in Australia.

MOSQUITOES ARE midge-like
flies. More than 3500 species have
been described worldwide so far. Some are
harmless, but the females of many species need the
protein in blood meals from living vertebrate
animals, including humans, for egg production and
it's this that can make them deadly. Most mosquito
species are dawn and dusk (crepuscular) feeders,
although some feed during the day.

Mosquito bites aren't venomous, but they can
carry viral and parasitic diseases that, between
them, have been the biggest killers in human
history (see page 71). Three genera contain species
of particular concern: *Aedes*, *Culex* and *Anopheles*.

It would be environmentally dangerous, and
probably impossible, to try to eradicate the
disease-carrying species. But vigilance to control
them in populated areas is essential. Screens, treated
nets, protective clothing and repellents are all
important responses because parasite and disease
cycles can be broken in localised areas when bites
are reduced.

The mosquito genera mentioned above are
distributed all over Australia, but the various
diseases and certain species are restricted to
particular regions, as discussed below. These
distributions also vary over time, with tropical
species extending their ranges all over the world as
the result of a warming climate.

The genus *Aedes* includes the dengue mosquito,
Aedes aegypti, which can carry dengue fever, as well
as several species that can carry Ross River fever.
A. aegypti can also carry yellow fever, although the
disease isn't present in Australia.

The genus *Culex* has some species that can carry
Ross River fever and different kinds of
encephalitis. The genus *Anopheles* has species that
can carry malaria, which isn't endemic in Australia.
The dog heartworm is carried by various species of
Aedes and *Culex* mosquitoes.

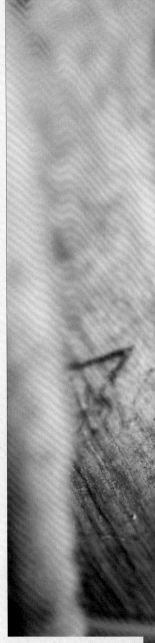

Anopheles farauti

INSECTS

Malaria

Malaria is caused by a blood parasite of the genus *Plasmodium*, which has a complex life cycle that involves mosquitoes.

Five species of this parasite exist in the world's tropics and are transmitted to people by certain *Anopheles* spp. mosquitoes. Malaria is by far the most significant mosquito-borne disease. The World Health Organization (WHO) estimates that, in 2012, there were 207 million malaria cases worldwide, and 627,000 deaths; children and pregnant women are most at risk.

Australia *had* endemic malaria, but after an eradication program WHO declared us "malaria-free" in 1981. Many cases are still reported here but come from bites sustained from travels in other countries. The most telling symptom is a very high fever occurring in cycles. Various drugs developed in recent decades have had good treatment results. But deadly new strains are emerging: too many returning tourists forget that preventative drugs must be taken for a period after staying in malaria zones.

Dengue, or breakbone, fever

Found throughout the tropics, the dengue virus is irregularly introduced to northern Queensland, where the only mainland mosquito carrier is found. Growing tourist traffic into Australia since the mid-1980s brings a new outbreak almost every year. The dengue mosquito breeds in very small bodies of water – like those in tin cans, gutters and pot-plant saucers around homes – and passes on the disease to humans in their saliva.

Each of the five known dengue strains causes fever with debilitating pain in muscles, joints and behind the eyes, and a rash. It can last for weeks, but after the initial disease abates it confers immunity to that strain. But getting different strains at different times can lead to dengue haemorrhagic fever, which can cause uncontrollable bleeding and death. Correct treatment, however, reduces the fatality rate to just 1 per cent. As yet there is no vaccine, so prevention is vital by removing mosquito breeding sites around populated areas.

The Asian tiger mosquito, *A. albopictus*, that's spreading worldwide, is a secondary carrier of dengue and primary carrier of the related Chikungunya virus. It is now in the Torres Straits Islands, but not on the mainland, where it could escalate the situation because it can survive temperate climates.

Zika virus

This virus, related to dengue, has been known in Ugandan monkeys since 1947. But it had laid low since then and has also been confused with dengue: symptoms include very similar fever, joint pains and rash. Up to 80 per cent of people do not react at all, and most of the rest are debilitated for days to weeks, but then recover.

What raised it to prominence recently was a 2013–14 outbreak in French Polynesia and a huge 2015–16 outbreak affecting more than one million people in Brazil. It was then found to increase birth defects, especially microcephaly (abnormally small heads). It is also possibly linked with the paralysis-causing Guillain-Barré syndrome. Several labs around the world are working on a vaccine because Zika is spread by the dengue mosquito, *Aedes aegypti,* and Asian Tiger mosquito, *Aedes albopictus.* Both species are hard to control and live alongside major human communities. In Australia, *A. aegypti* is found along the Queensland coast, from the top of Cape York to near Rockhampton.

Ross River fever

Named for the Ross River near Townsville, Queensland, this Australian virus is now active from northern Tasmania to most of the mainland outside the interior, and has recently spread into the Pacific. It appears similar to German measles, with skin rashes as the early symptoms, but the arthritic joint pains that follow can be debilitating for months. Another difference is that children are less likely than adults to get ill.

The virus is carried by both the *Culex* and *Aedes* mosquitoes, and other mammals, particularly kangaroos and wallabies, serve as hosts. Western Australia has most of the 5000 or so cases reported each year. A vaccine is in the developmental stage.

Encephalitis

Australian, or Murray Valley, encephalitis has irregular outbreaks in many major river systems on the mainland, particularly in Western Australia's Kimberley and the Northern Territory. Water birds carry it and the common banded mosquito, *Culex annulirostris,* can spread it between humans and other mammals. Only one in 1000 people contracting the virus will develop the disease, but the onset can be life-threatening. Symptoms include severe headaches, fever, stiffness and an aversion to light. It can result in permanent brain damage.

The related Japanese encephalitis, which is equally dangerous and common in South-East Asia, is endemic in the Torres Strait and PNG. Queensland health authorities have reported one case of the virus. There is a possibility it could spread further south in Australia, where feral pigs and birds can serve as a host.

Aedes albopictus

Prevention is better than cure

ABOUT 5000 PEOPLE in Australia become sick each year following mosquito bites. Most commonly, they fall victim to Ross River virus or Barmah Forest virus transmitted in the infected spit of female mosquitoes as they take blood meals.

If you can stop mosquitoes biting, you're obviously less likely to be infected and become ill. There are a few ways you can very effectively reduce your personal risk of being bitten. Avoiding wetlands and bushland areas where mosquitoes breed is important. Avoiding these places when mosquities are most active – dawn and dusk – is also beneficial. Be mindful too that mosquito populations are usually greatest about a week after heavy rain or king tides.

Covering up with a long-sleeved shirt, long pants and closed shoes also provides good protection. If you're camping out, sleeping under a bed net will help. Treating your clothing and bed net with insecticides (e.g. permethrin) can provide extra protection.

The most common way to stop mosquitoes biting is by using a topical insect repellent. Always choose a product registered with the Australian Pesticides and Veterinary Medicines Authority (APVMA), which checks for safety and effectiveness.

The products that provide the longest lasting protection are those containing DEET or picaridin. These active ingredients are commonly found in commercial insect repellent formulations available at supermarkets and pharmacies.

It doesn't matter whether you're using a roll-on, spray or lotion, it is the active ingredients that keep mosquitoes away. Just make sure you apply a thin layer on all exposed skin, a dab 'here and there' won't work. You'll have to reapply after swimming and strenuous, sweaty exercise too.

If you prefer a plant-based repellent, such as tea-tree oil or lemon eucalyptus oil, be aware that these products generally don't provide protection for as long as the other repellents. They still work, but you'll need to reapply far more frequently.

When choosing an insect repellent, note that the strength of it will determine how long it lasts, not how many mosquitoes it'll stop from biting. If you're only going to be outside for a short period, there is really no need to use a high-dose formulation. However, if you're planning a fishing trip, bushwalk or other activities that bring you into contact with mosquitoes for longer, you'll need a stronger formulation.

Putting on repellent can often be annoying. It is tempting to try mosquito repellent wrist bands, patches and other gimmicks. These don't provide enough protection and should be avoided.

Mosquitoes are a natural part of our local wetlands and while some bite, many rarely cause problems for people. In fact, they're useful food for birds, bats, fish and frogs! If you're enjoying the Australian environment, mosquitoes are just part of the experience.

By Dr Cameron Webb, University of Sydney and NSW Health Pathology

INSECTS

PLATYPUS

Ornithorhynchus anatinus

Other common name: Duck-billed platypus

MAMMAL

DUCK BILLED PLATYPUSES belong to a special order of mammals known as monotremes, meaning one-holed, a reference to the cloaca, which is a single opening that is used for both reproduction and excretion. The group also includes the echidna and is unique in that both of these mammalian species are egg-layers.

Platypuses are found in freshwater systems and, because of their secretive nature, are rarely seen by people though they are fairly common in their natural type of habitat. They are superbly adapted to their aquatic world with a double coat of fur for insulation and a bill that is believed to be able to detect electric currents generated by the muscle activity of small prey and the weak electrical fields caused by water flowing over stationary objects.

The tail is used to store fat and is a handy stabiliser under water. The males have a sharp hollow spur about 15mm in length on the inside of each hind leg. The spur is connected to a venom gland that enlarges during the breeding season when males are more aggressive. A sting from this spur can cause severe pain in humans but is not lethal. Swelling can occur at the puncture site and spread throughout the affected limb. There is evidence to suggest that this pain can develop into a temporary increase in pain sensitivity that can last for days and even months. Most stings happen when a platypus is being handled so care must be taken to avoid the hind legs, and if handling is unavoidable, for instance in the case of rescuing an injured individual, picking up by the latter end of the tail is recommended.

First aid includes restricting movement of the affected limb, keeping the victim still and calm, and the application of an icepack or local anaesthetic cream to reduce the severity of the pain. After that, seek medical help.

Greater blue-ringed octopus

SEA

Sharks, crocodiles, fishes, jellyfish
and other marine creatures that
bite and sting

Shortfin mako shark

JUST FOUR SHARK SPECIES ARE RESPONSIBLE FOR MOST HUMAN ATTACKS. THE BAD NEWS IS ALL OCCUR IN AUSTRALIAN WATERS. THE GOOD NEWS IS A BEE IS MORE LIKELY TO KILL YOU.

SHARKS

SUPERBLY ADAPTED and stunningly graceful in their environment, the shark species considered dangerous to humans are among the ocean's top predators and play a critical role in maintaining the health of their ecosystems.

More than 400 shark species have been described worldwide, and of these only about 30 have been confirmed in or suspected of unprovoked attacks on humans. The incidence of shark attacks remains very small, but has grown during the past century, almost certainly because an increasing number of people are spending more recreation time in the ocean. The International Shark Attack File, based in Florida, USA, reported 98 unprovoked attacks worldwide in 2015, which was the highest on record. Just six were fatal. In 2016 there were 17 unprovoked attacks in Australian waters, of which two proved fatal.

If you're a keen ocean-user (swimmer, snorkeller, surfer or diver), there are a number of simple behaviours you can enact to reduce the already remote risk of an attack (see *To reduce the risk of shark attack*, page 109). Most 'dangerous' sharks belong to the order Lamniformes, or mackerel sharks – including the great white shark, and Carcharhiniformes, or ground sharks – including the tiger, bull and oceanic whitetip sharks.

4 SPECIES **1** DEATH/YR

ON AVERAGE, **1 FATAL UNPROVOKED ATTACK** PER YEAR IN AUSTRALIA IN THE PAST 50 YEARS

BULL SHARK

Carcharhinus leucas

Other common names: estuary shark,
freshwater whaler, river whaler, Zambezi shark

A MATURE BULL SHARK is a stocky, solid fish of an unremarkable dull grey colour, fading to a white belly. Juveniles may have black fin tips, which fade as they grow. In profile, adults have a deep, thick torso, the bulk becoming even more pronounced with age.

The head is short and broad, with relatively small eyes. The first dorsal fin is broad-based and close to being an equilateral triangle. The name, bull shark, is derived from its bull-like thick, heavy body, short blunt head and aggressive 'bullish' nature.

Found in tropical to warm temperate regions, bull sharks have a habit of dwelling near murky river mouths and estuaries, which puts them in direct contact with humans. This species is often found living in tidal rivers, even moving into fresh water such as the Mississippi River, in the USA, or freshwater Lake Nicaragua, in central America. Their tolerance of freshwater, or low-salinity, environments is a unique characteristic. While other species may occasionally enter estuaries or river mouths, bulls seem to prefer the lower salinity, especially for birthing.

Young bull sharks, born at about 70cm, will stay in low-salinity areas, avoiding other marine fish and shark predators, and move out into the ocean environment only when they have become sexually mature. Adults grow to 4m in length and may weigh more than 300kg. An average-sized adult is about 2.5m long, with males being slightly smaller than females.

Because river and estuary zones are typically low visibility, these sharks hunt more by scent and by detecting vibrations in the water than sight. Combine murky river water with human activity and a shark with a bullish nature, and it's no wonder this species has been implicated in many unprovoked attacks.

With a broad, indiscriminate diet – from fish and crabs to dolphins, birds and carrion – the bull shark will take just about anything it chances upon. When in feeding mode, it is bold and aggressive, charging and moving far quicker than its rotund shape would suggest it can.

GREAT WHITE SHARK

Carcharodon carcharias
Other common names: white death, white pointer

THE GREAT WHITE belongs to the Lamniforme, or mackerel, shark order. It lacks a nictitating membrane on the eyes – a translucent eyelid that protects the eye while feeding. Instead, Lamniformes roll their eyes back into their skull. The great white is the most notorious of all sharks, the largest predatory fish on the planet, with more unprovoked fatal attacks on humans than any other species.

The great white shark is light to charcoal grey or dark brown on the back, often with a bronze sheen, fading to pale grey on the sides then abruptly white on the belly. This shark's conical snout is often heavily scarred, usually caused by the teeth and claws of seals fighting for their lives. The snout shape, massive body size and large black eyes make them easy to identify, especially because they are quite curious around boats, giving the occupants a clear view.

The largest specimen reliably measured to date was 6.4m long and weighed 3324kg. The average size of a mature white shark is 4.6m. An adult will have up to 300 teeth arranged in up to seven rows. When outer teeth are broken off from the jaw cartilage, the next teeth rotate forward. The teeth are, literally, razor sharp, able to inflict massive, fatal wounds with just one bite.

The great white is a stealth hunter, attacking seals, dolphins and small whales from behind and below. Normal behaviour is for it to hit hard with a single bite, inflicting a large, deep wound. The shark then retreats, waiting for the prey to bleed out, before coming back in to feed safely. Human attacks follow the same pattern: surfers, swimmers and divers are hit without warning, and, if not rescued, bleed out and are consumed.

Despite their reputation, great white sharks are now protected in many countries due to a low birth rate and high casualty rate, usually in nets set for other species.

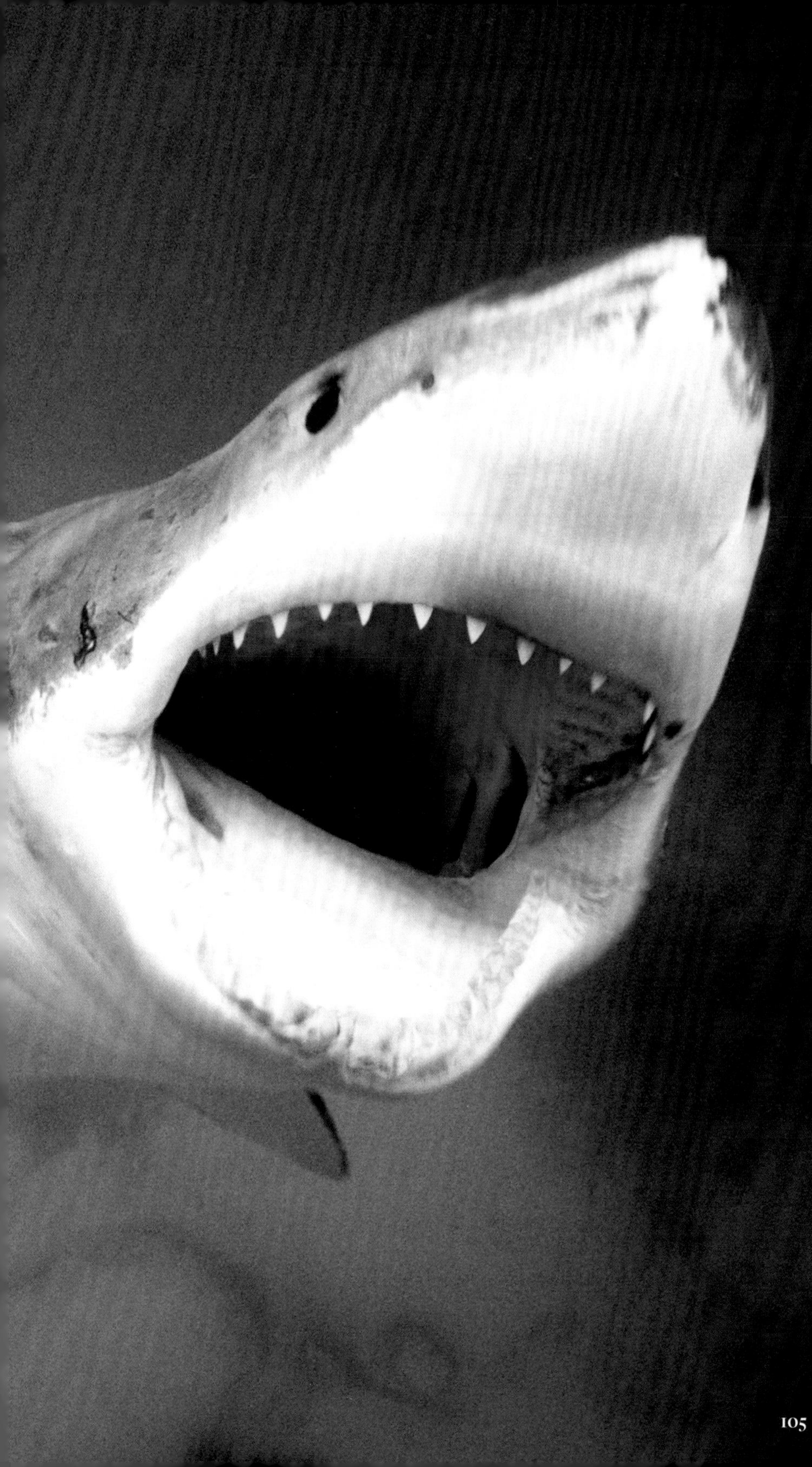

SHARK ATTACKS BY NUMBERS

THE LOCAL AUTHORITY on shark attacks is Taronga Conservation Society Australia, which has maintained the Australian Shark Attack File (ASAF) for more than three decades, gathering extensive information on shark and human encounters in Australian waters during that period. The ASAF is based at Taronga Zoo in Sydney and works closely with the International Shark Attack File (ISAF), based at the Florida Museum of Natural History, USA.

Key points from the ASAF and the Royal Life Saving Society include:

Since 1791,

691

unprovoked shark attacks have been recorded in Australian waters, 185 fatal.

Between 2013 and 2016 there have been, on average, two fatal unprovoked shark attacks in Australia each year.

There have been no unprovoked
SHARK FATALITIES
in Tasmania since 1993, Victoria since 1987, and NT since 1934.

Between **2006** and **2016**, an average of

280

Australians drowned each year, about one-sixth of them at the beach.

During 2006–16, an average of **12** rock fishers per year were swept off rocks and drowned.

The ISAF notes that, during **2004–13,** seven Americans were killed in unprovoked shark attacks. In the same period, **301** Americans were killed in dog attacks and **361** Americans died after being caught in a rip current.

During recent decades the average number of unprovoked shark attacks has increased. In the 1990s the average was 6.5 per year; during 2003–13 this rose to 13 per year.

Between 2006 and 2016, there was an average of 16 diving-related deaths per year.

Statistics from ASAF website and the Royal Life Saving Society – Australia National Fatal Drowning Database

Grey nurse shark

1ST PERSON

No photos allowed

Kelvin Aitken is warned about his behaviour while intruding in shark habitat.

THE GREY NURSE shark (*Carcharias taurus*) is a favourite aquarium species. It's sociable, grows to an impressive 3m and has a fierce, toothy countenance. In winter, large numbers of grey nurse can be found around Big Seal Rock, on the central New South Wales coast.

The dive site at Big Seal consists of a sandy gutter fronting a reef wall with a shallow cave. The idea is to sit in the gutter and let the sharks come to you. They are naturally curious, so once you settle, they will sidle up, often within touching distance.

I wanted a silhouette photo of a shark against the bright surface. During the previous week I had come close a few times but with other divers about, the simple shot proved elusive. By the end of my last dive, I was becoming frustrated. With about a minute left, a single mature grey nurse came in, swimming above and towards me. Perfect. But at the last second it began to turn away. My camera rig had long metal arms holding the strobe flash units, and I reached out to put the flash in front of the shark, to turn it back overhead.

The shark didn't like that.

With blinding speed, it bit my strobe, shaking its head violently and almost tearing the camera from my hands. It spat out the strobe, gave me a disdainful look, flexed its toothy jaws, then casually swam away. I was uninjured, but overcome by shock, guilt and embarrassment – the latter two because I'd stooped to such a cheap trick. I swam to the anchor rope and shamefully ascended.

Later that night, I removed a number of tooth chips from my strobe, feeling grateful the shark had chomped on it and not on my head.

OCEANIC WHITETIP SHARK

Carcharhinus longimanus

Other common names: oceanic
whitetipped whaler, whitetip whaler

OCEANIC WHITETIP belongs to the ground shark order (or Carcharhiniformes) within which it is placed in the Carcharhinidae family, otherwise known as requiem sharks, a grim name for a dangerous group.

Oceanic whitetips are impressive, stocky animals with distinctive rounded tips on the dorsal and pectoral fins. These fin tips also feature white markings, as does the lower caudal fin. In combination, these few features make these sharks fairly easy to identify. They vary in overall colour from dark to light grey to dull brown, sometimes with a bronze or blue tinge. Mostly, their overall colour is nondescript, their main feature being bright, rounded fin tips. Maximum length is 4m but are more commonly 2.5–3m.

This species is primarily a deep-sea nomad, covering large distances across all oceans in tropical to temperate regions as well as the Mediterranean and Red seas. In short, this is a cosmopolitan shark that loves to travel.

Divers rarely encounter the species because it seldom comes close to shore, though can be found near shallow reefs that border deep ocean channels. Spearfishers searching for tuna, mahi mahi or other open ocean (pelagic) species in tropical regions are more likely to come across a single animal, attracted by the diver's baits, vibrations or scent of speared fish.

They are known to form loose groups when a food source is found, such as a whale carcass, and are often seen following tropical toothed whales, such as short-finned pilot whales, and scavenging off their scraps. Being open-ocean dwellers, oceanic whitetips respond quickly to the rare appearance of any potential food, the result being a predator that is very bold, aggressive and without the inherent caution shown by most other shark species. Divers and swimmers (usually shipwreck survivors) can be attacked without warning. The oceanic whitetip's size, speed and aggression make it a very dangerous species.

TO REDUCE THE RISK OF SHARK ATTACK

the Australian Shark Attack File advises:

● Always swim at beaches patrolled by surf lifesavers. They are there to keep an eye on your safety, look for signs of danger and assist if you get into trouble.

● **Do not swim, dive or surf where dangerous sharks are known to congregate.**

● Always swim, dive or surf with other people. Their presence may deter an attack and your companion can assist if you get into trouble or are bitten.

● **Never swim in dirty or turbid water because there there is little chance of seeing a shark in these conditions.**

● Avoid swimming at dusk, dawn or night. Many sharks are more active during these times and in low-light conditions you may not be able to see one approaching.

● **Avoid swimming well offshore, near deep channels or along drop-offs to deeper water. Sharks are more likely to inhabit deeper water.**

● Avoid entering the ocean near a river mouth, especially after a storm. Rain can wash potential food items into the sea that might attract fish, including sharks.

● **If schooling fish congregate in large numbers, leave the water. Sharks could be feeding on baitfish schools.**

● Never swim near people fishing or spearfishing because these activities can attract sharks.

● **Don't be fooled into thinking dolphins in the area indicate the absence of sharks. Dolphins and sharks sometimes feed together and some sharks feed on dolphins.**

● Kayakers should 'raft up' together if a large shark is seen in the area. This makes for a larger object that a shark may not be interested in.

● **Do not swim with pets or other domestic animals. Sharks can be attracted to non-aquatic animals in the water.**

● Look carefully before jumping into the water from a boat or wharf. People have jumped on top of sharks!

● **Be careful wading through shallow water because wobbegong sharks are known to hide among kelp in shallow water and it is easy to accidentally step on one and get bitten without knowing it was there.**

● Don't wear shiny jewellery while you are in the water. It can reflect light in a way that resembles fish scales, which can attract sharks.

● **If a shark is sighted in the area leave the water as quickly and calmly as possible.**

TIGER SHARK
Galeocerdo cuvier

Other common names: man-eater shark,
leopard shark

WITH A BLUNT, almost square snout and dark, vertical bands on its back and flanks, this large species is easily distinguished from any other. At maturity the bands may fade almost completely to an overall mid-to-dark grey – their striped, tiger-like pattern, giving the species its most common name.

Tiger sharks have large black eyes that allow this species to see well during both day and night. Twilight and night-time is their more active hunting period.

The teeth, which have a distinctive and unique jagged cockscomb shape, are able to saw through scales, bone and even the armour-like shells of mature sea turtles. As for most shark species, the teeth are arranged in rows, rotating forward as outer teeth break off.

About 50cm long at birth and distinctly striped as juveniles, tigers are the largest tropical shark species: they can grow to 7m and weigh more than 800kg, although 3–4m individuals are more common. One shark taken off South-East Asia measured 7.4m and weighed 3110kg. Individuals over 3.5m become very deep-bodied and heavy.

This species occurs in all oceans from tropical to warm temperate regions. In deep areas they may range from near the surface down to 400m, but are more often found on shallow reefs, in bays or estuaries, in as little as knee-deep water.

Famously and frighteningly, the tiger shark has an indiscriminate appetite. Objects as bizarre and diverse as plastic toys, shoes, bottles and farm animals have been found in tigers' stomachs. They will feed on just about anything that crosses their path, from reef fish to whale carcasses, shells, crabs and octopus to birds and carrion.

Tiger sharks have attacked, killed and even eaten humans. Their regular forays into murky inshore areas, such as estuaries, tidal river mouths and shallow bays, along with their massive size, indiscriminate appetite and aggressive nature, make them a real danger to swimmers and waders. They are second only to the great white shark in recorded unprovoked attacks on humans.

Tropical encounter

Kylie Maguire develops a deeper respect for sharks.

I N 2012, on a ship-board adventure in Tonga, I met a new friend, Kim, who'd come to fulfil her dream of swimming with whales. One day she suggested a 1500m swim between two nearby islands. We took an inflatable kayak so one of us could swim while the other paddled.

It was my turn to swim on the way back and I remember saying, "It's not shark-feeding time yet is it?" But we shrugged off the thought, I put on my free-diving fins and off we went. There was a sand bank for the first few hundred metres, then it dropped off quickly. About a third of the way across this deep water, I felt spooked and thought I'd seen something. Once again I shrugged it off, but two strokes later felt a bump.

What happened next is unclear to me, it happened so fast. I think I retracted my legs, then was bitten on my left buttock and inner thigh. I called for help then put my head in the water to see where the shark was, and met it face to face. It simply turned away, and I got onto the kayak in lightning speed, losing a fin along the way. The shark is likely to have been either a grey reef or Galapagos shark, but we sure didn't hang around to I.D. it!

I'd had such an adrenaline surge that at first I wasn't sure I'd been bitten. I didn't visually check the wound, but felt around until I realised that I had. We had a VHF radio and I began to call the island as Kim paddled to it. A yachtie responded, asking if I was okay. My response was something like: "Yes, I'm fine. I've just been bitten by a shark and I'm trying to contact my boat." Close to the island I yelled as loud as I could for help. The island was an eco-retreat that hosts about eight guests and it happend that two of them at that time were doctors.

I was stretchered on the kayak to the high-speed whale-watching boat, which took me to Neiafu, the Vava'u group's main island, and its Prince Wellington Ngu Hospital. I had surgery on my buttock that night, and four days later was medevaced back to Australia for surgery on my leg. All up I was in hospital for 11 days and three weeks later was on the Sea Shepherd vessel *Sam Simon* for an anti-whaling campaign.

These days, any chance I get, I emphasise how amazing sharks are, and their importance in our oceans. My experience hasn't deterred me from sharks, only deepened my respect for them.

SHORTFIN MAKO

Isurus oxyrinchus

Other common names: blue pointer,
bonito shark, mackerel shark, snapper shark

MAKO SHARKS include two species, shortfin and longfin. Shortfins are found offshore but rarely in water below 16°C. The most obvious characteristics of makos are a sharply pointed conical snout, large black eyes and protruding snaggle-teeth. They also display a startling electric blue colour when alive, dark on the back, blending to a pure white belly. Their generic name, *Isurus*, means 'equal tail', referring to the same-sized upper and lower tail lobes, a form also found on fast-swimming fish such as tuna and marlin. Due to their offshore habitat, shortfin makos are usually only encountered by swimmers or divers on reefs or islands close to deep oceanic waters, or if prey species, such as tuna, come in close to shore. They are probably the fastest of all sharks and are capable of spectacular leaps out of the water. Their speed and size (up to 4m) coupled with an unpredictable nature make them dangerous, particularly when bait or prey species are in the water.

SHARKS

BRONZE WHALER

Carcharhinus brachyurus

Other common names: cocktail shark, copper shark, black-tipped whaler

THE BRONZE WHALER has a broad, flat snout, coppery sheen over a grey to bronze coloured upper body and a white belly. Unlike makos, their teeth are inconspicuous unless feeding.

Whalers will follow seasonal schooling fish right into beach surf zones, bringing them into contact with divers, swimmers and surfers. Although not known as 'man-eaters', they have attacked people, mostly in response to splashing or bait in the water. Their razor-sharp teeth, used to tear apart fast-swimming fish, can leave a massive, potenitally fatal wound. More attacks and deaths have been attributed to the bronze whaler than the mako, primarily due to their inshore habitat.

Both mako and bronze whaler sharks have been responsible for unprovoked attacks on humans, some fatal. While not as large as the great white or tiger, these species make up for it with an aggressive nature and wide distribution.

Saltwater crocodile

ENCOUNTERS WITH ADULT SALTWATER CROCS
RARELY END WELL – THE BEST PROTECTION AGAINST
THESE REPTILES IS TO STAY OUT OF THEIR WAY.

CROCODILES

MEMBERS OF THE order Crocodilia, which include
crocodiles and alligators, are truly just a few steps from
the dinosaurs. Their ancestors survived the Cretaceous–
Paleogene extinction event of 66 million years ago and many
crocodile species still thrive today.

Among them are two found in Australia, the saltwater, or estuarine,
crocodile, and the smaller freshwater crocodile. These magnificent
predators are found across northern Australia, from about Broome on
the West Australian coast to Rockhampton, Queensland, in the east.
The common names of both species can't be relied on to describe
their habitat: 'salties' are found in fresh water, sometimes well away
from the coast, and 'freshies' are often seen in low-lying billabongs
near the tidal reaches of rivers and coastal wetlands.

Crocodiles are opportunistic carnivores and their danger to
humans is largely a function of size. The freshwater species rarely
exceeds 3m in length and has a more slender snout and smaller teeth
than the saltie; while freshies have been known to bite humans
(see page 119), they aren't regarded as killers. The saltie, in contrast,
can grow to 5m or more, with large individuals weighing close to
a tonne. After many decades of being hunted for its skin, the species
has been fully protected throughout its range since the early 1970s
and both the total population and the average size of individuals
has increased.

Today, monitoring and management sees many salties that
threaten human safety caught and removed. But this is one animal
that should never be underestimated. Visitors to areas inhabited by
crocodiles should remain vigilant (see *Staying smart in croc country*,
page 118).

1-2 DEATHS
4-10 ATTACKS

CROCODILES KILL **1-2 PEOPLE** A YEAR IN
NORTHERN AUSTRALIA AND INJURE ANOTHER **4-10**

Crocodylus porosus

Saltwater crocodile

CROCODILES

GENUS *Crocodylus*

SALTWATER OR ESTUARINE CROCODILE *Crocodylus porosus*

FRESHWATER OR JOHNSTONE'S CROCODILE *Crocodylus johnstoni*

IN AUSTRALIA, we take comfort in knowing there are no wild animals lurking out there, ready to launch an unprovoked attack. Provided we watch our step and avoid harassing the wildlife, it will leave us alone. This is true on land, but the northern rivers and estuaries are another world altogether.

For saltwater crocodiles, there is no difference between a wallaby drinking from the water's edge, a dog cooling off, or a human having a swim. All are a potential meal. Crocodiles have been ambushing prey from under water since the time of dinosaurs. When cataclysmic events shook up the world more than 60 million years ago, causing mass extinctions and altering the course of evolution, crocodiles endured. They are much the same now as they were then.

The crocodilian design is obviously a superb one. The eyes are placed high on the head and valvular nostrils lie on the top of the snout, so they can see and breathe above water while barely

Crocodylus johnstoni

Freshwater crocodile

breaking the surface. The clawed feet are strongly webbed, the tail is laterally flattened and the body and snout are streamlined – all of which allows for easy propulsion through the water. The rows of conical teeth and powerful jaws are designed to snap shut and hold fast.

Of the two Australian species, the one of least concern is the freshwater crocodile, which has a slender snout suited to sidewise swiping at fish. With an average length of 2m, it is not regarded as dangerous to humans, though there are cases where a hand, foot or leg has been mistaken for a tasty barramundi.

The saltwater crocodile ('saltie') has a broader, more powerful snout to deal with larger mammals. At 5m-plus in length, these animals have a bite that can snap a buffalo's leg. Yet when their eggs hatch those same jaws can delicately remove tiny baby crocs and carry them safely to the water.

Salties are extremely dangerous animals if we enter their domain. A swim in the tropical heat is highly tempting but any large body of water, salt or fresh, in the continents's north can potentially conceal a croc. There are plenty of warning signs across northern Australia, so heed them. More importantly, always remember that the key to crocodiles' success as predators has been their ability to remain invisible for as long as it takes. If you can't see a croc, it does not mean a croc can't see you!

STAYING SMART
IN CROC COUNTRY

SALTWATER CROCODILE numbers have increased since their protection (in 1969 in WA, 1971 in NT and 1974 in Queensland) and more people are visiting their habitat areas, which are often in isolated locations. Queensland, NT and WA wildlife authorities urge visitors to be aware ('croc wise') and act with caution: know the risks and make informed, sensible choices.

**KEY SAFETY POINTS
TO REMEMBER ARE:**

● **Always obey crocodile warning signs and only swim in safe designated areas. If there isn't a safe swimming sign, don't swim.**

● Avoid the water's edge wherever possible.

● **Don't paddle, clean fish, prepare food or wash at the water's edge.**

● Stand at least 5m back from the water's edge when fishing; never stand on logs or branches overhanging the water.

● **Don't hang arms or legs out of a boat when on the water and if you fall out of a boat, get out of the water as quickly as possible.**

● Don't dispose of food scraps and fish offal in the water; use bins or bury it at least 2m from the water's edge.

● **Stay away from crocodile slide marks and nest mounds.**

● Camp at least 2m above the high water mark and at least 50m from the water's edge.

● **Avoid camping in places where native animals and domestic stock drink. Never leave food scraps, fish frames or bait at your campsite and always check that previous campers have not left these behind.**

● Don't feed or encourage, harass or interfere with crocodiles, even small ones.

● **Be extra vigilant at night and during the breeding season: September–April.**

1ST PERSON

Freshie with attitude

Daryl Byrne survives an unexpected close encounter in croc country.

EVERYONE IN camp at Australian Geographic Society's 2013 scientific expedition at El Questro Wilderness Park, in Western Australia's East Kimberley, had been warned about crocs. With a few exceptions, we knew the famous 'El Q' gorges were mostly free of dangerous 'salties' and okay for swimming. The resident 'freshies' might mistake flapping feet or legs for fish, but you'd be unlucky.

One afternoon I went walking with friends up Amalia Gorge. It was a 40°C day and we made several stops for cooling swims. At one, we met some people who said they'd seen a small 'freshie' sunning itself at 'first pool'. On our way back down the gorge we decided to jump off the 3m-high rock there for a final dip and were floating across the pool, chatting away, when I saw something below me through the tannin-stained water.

"I think there's a croc right under me," I managed to call out, before it propelled up, bit at my right leg and I felt a tug and some pain around my knee. "It's just bitten me!" I yelled, my attempt to stay cool shattered by the pitch of my voice. Now, I've got a reputation for having a sense of humour, and they started with comments like

"yeah, sure Daz" and "pull the other one". I quickly swam to the other side, cautious not to break the water's surface too much, while scanning the depths for signs of my attacker. When I stood up there were croc-teeth marks above my knee and on my shin, and blood was flowing fairly steadily, if not dangerously, from the wound. I recall that those left in the water exited quite quickly at that point. Once safely ashore, there were many calls of "Wow! Check it out," and "Crikey, he's not kidding."

The shakes set in from the adrenaline surge as I tried to climb around the pool to where we'd left our bags. (I certainly wasn't swimming back!) As we gathered our stuff and photographed the wound, I thought how lucky I was it didn't bite me where it may have hit an artery.

As we readied to go, up floated the croc in the middle of the pool, giving us the eye. It was a real beauty; someone said about 150cm, but I know it was at least as tall as me, and I must be, oh, 3m at least. It was still floating there when the people we'd met earlier came along. I told them about the bite, showed them the wound, and pointed to the croc. "Definitely not the little guy we saw earlier," was their conclusion.

Jelly blubber

JELLYFISH CAPTURE PREY WITH VENOM-EQUIPPED STINGING CELLS. MANY AUSTRALIAN SPECIES CAN GIVE PAINFUL STINGS, AND SOME ARE AMONG EARTH'S MOST DANGEROUS CREATURES.

JELLYFISH & THEIR KIN

G IVEN THEIR diversity and prevalence, it's a fine thing that only a few members of the phylum Cnidaria create problems for humans. The cnidarians include jellyfish, box jellyfish, sea anemones and corals, among others – more than 9000 species have so far been described worldwide. The feature that unites them is the presence of specialised stinging cells called nematocysts that are mainly used for capturing prey.

The danger of these animals is related primarily to the volume of nematocysts that come into contact with a victim's skin. The sessile (immobile) types such as sea anemones and corals are generally of less concern because a human must brush against them for the stinging cells to fire. The mobile species are a much bigger worry and their danger is influenced by the number and length of their tentacles and the number of nematocysts they bear. The box jellyfish, *Chironex fleckeri*, which has many long tentacles densely packed with nematocysts, has accounted for the majority of deaths in Australian waters from jellyfish stings.

While it's true that bluebottles – also cnidarians – can spoil a nice day at the beach, the stings of most of these jelly-like sea creatures produce little more than mild irritation and perhaps itching if they come into contact with humans.

70
DEATHS

AT LEAST **70 PEOPLE** HAVE BEEN KILLED BY THE STINGS OF BOX JELLYFISH IN AUSTRALIAN WATERS

BOX JELLYFISH AND OTHER CUBOZOANS

FAMILIES Chirodropidae and Carybdeidae

BOX JELLYFISH *Chironex fleckeri*
MORBAKKA, FIRE JELLY *Morbakka fenneri*
SEA WASP *Carybdea marsupialis*

THE DEADLY box jellyfish, *Chironex fleckeri*, frequents northern Australian waters from spring to autumn, and the species' 70 confirmed human fatalities have mostly occurred during October–May. But when conditions are right, it may be found in other months and some fatalities have occurred in Northern Territory waters at other times during the year. Box jellies are also found in waters north of Australia, from Papua New Guinea to the Philippines and Vietnam and west to Indonesia, Malaysia and India.

C. fleckeri is the largest cubozoan jellyfish, with a bell up to 30cm in diameter, but younger animals with a bell about a third that size are capable of deadly stings. Up to 15 tentacles trail from each corner of the bell. Each tentacle may be up to 3m long and contain thousands of individual nematocysts. The box jellyfish is an active swimmer by day, when it hunts prey – mainly small fish and prawns, which it will follow into shallow water off beaches.

It's the tentacle size and nematocyst density that make the box jellyfish particularly dangerous. If enough of the tentacles come into contact with a person's skin, the many small doses of venom injected by the nematocysts can combine into a deadly volume; 3–5m of tentacles can kill an adult in less than three minutes. The venom mainly affects the heart and respiratory system and deaths are often due to cardiac arrest or respiratory failure. The venom also causes intense localised pain – a 'hot-iron'-like burning sensation. In non-lethal cases, the pain often persists for hours and leaves scars at the sting site – a legacy of tissue destruction. The effects are particularly dangerous for small children and the elderly.

Other members of the family Chirodropidae, and some of the family Carybdeidae, have in the past been collectively known as sea wasps, a confusing term that should be abandoned. They generally occur in tropical waters, and while not as dangerous as the box jellyfish, have stings that can cause great pain and even death. Most species have multiple tentacles on the four bell corners, but their bells and tentacles are generally smaller than those of the box jellyfish. Some species have only a single tentacle on each corner. For first aid for stings by box jellyfish and related species, see page 185.

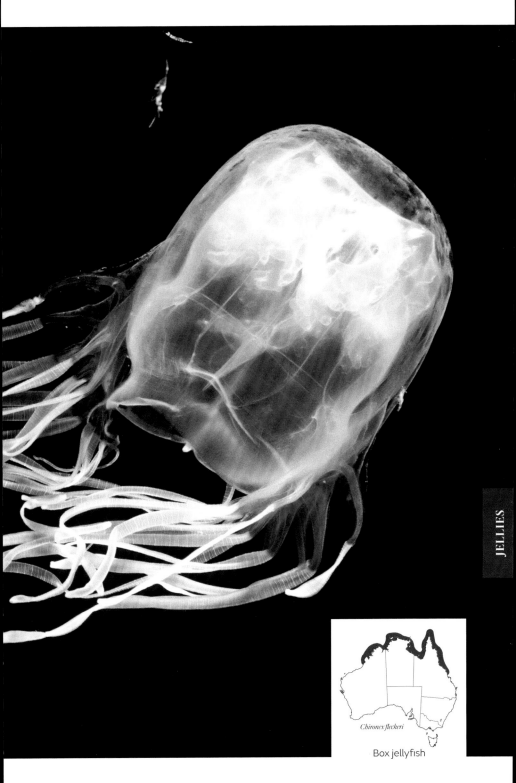

JELLIES

Chironex fleckeri

Box jellyfish

IRUKANDJI JELLYFISH

FAMILIES Alatinidae, Carukiidae, Tamoyidae

SPECIES *Carukia barnesi, Malo kingi, Alatina alata, Morbakka fenneri, Malo maximus, Carukia shinju, Malo bella, Keesingia gigas*

Morbakka fenneri

IRUKANDJI IS THE collective name given to species of box jellyfish that have just one tentacle arising in each lower corner of the bell. They are usually transparent and not seen, except for larger species. The tentacles may be a few centimetres to 60cm in length.

Irukandji is a name that causes a lot of confusion. At one time it referred to just one small jellyfish – *Carukia barnesi*. However, 'Irukandji syndrome' also refers to a set of symptoms associated with stings from *C. barnesi* and several other species. The name Irukandji is therefore difficult to use for identification because there are now at least 14 species known to cause the syndrome, although some are yet to be scientifically identified and described. Each causes the 'basic' Irukandji syndrome, and, depending on which species is responsible, symptoms may be even more varied, more severe and, at times, life-threatening.

Although Irukandji are often found in deep water, swarms can form at the surface at swimming beaches. The bell can be just 2.5–3.5cm in diameter when contracted, but some 60–70cm when the jellyfish is 'fishing' for prey of small fish. Little is currently known of any of the species' life cycles.

Irukandji

A sting usually results in a small mark, often the shape of the jellyfish bell, that is very difficult, if not almost impossible to see; less often, tentacle marks may be seen. A couple of moments after the sting from the bell, the skin may develop a mild redness and a 'goose-pimple' effect that can last for 30 minutes or so. The reddish imprint, if visible, may last several days.

Irukandji syndrome describes the symptoms that arise from an Irukandji sting. It usually occurs about 30 minutes after a seemingly minor skin sting and follows a sequence of symptoms. It begins with severe lower back pain and cramps in all limbs, extending into the abdomen and chest. Profuse sweating, anxiety and restlessness follow, then intractable nausea, vomiting and headaches. Very high blood pressure may also develop, which may be life-threatening, as well as heart failure needing assisted breathing in a hospital's intensive care unit. High blood pressure has caused stroke and death in two Irukandji sting cases in Australian waters in recent years.

FIRST AID and further treatment

Stay with the victim; reassure and encourage them to rest, as muscle activity increases the heart rate, absorption and systemic dissipation of venom. Douse the area with vinegar: although adherent tentacles may not be visible, skin scrapings show that, as with all jellyfish stings, there will be remaining unfired nematocysts.

Transport the victim to hospital by ambulance. Ambulances carry magnesium sulfate, which can reduce all symptoms, and glyceryl trinitrate, which can reduce raised blood pressure if it continues after the magnesium is given. Unless a careful history is taken, Irukandji syndrome can – and has been – confused with conditions that may produce similar symptoms, namely heart attack and decompression sickness.

1ST
PERSON

A world of Irukandji pain

Marine scientist **Jamie Seymour** survived a jellyfish
sting beyond his worst nightmare.

ASSOCIATE PROFESSOR Jamie Seymour of James Cook University is a serious researcher with a decidedly comical nickname – the Jelly Dude from Nemo Land. For the past two decades he has studied venomous animals, with a focus on dangerous jellyfish, especially the box jellyfish *Chironex fleckeri* and Irukandji types. He takes a highly involved approach that's given him a particularly unique insight into these creatures and their dangers.

"I've been stung badly three times and had several hundred minor stings," he told a *60 minutes*/ninemsn online forum, in 2009. "It's not something I'm proud of."

A few years earlier, in 2006, Jamie told AUSTRALIAN GEOGRAPHIC writer Karen McGhee about his experience of an Irukandji sting. It was his 11th such sting and, as Karen wrote then, "Given his description of the

aftermath, you'd think he'd be more careful."

"It's beyond your worst nightmare," Dr Seymour said at the time. "Stomach cramps, nausea, vomiting and severe pins and needles in the lower joints and this racking ache throughout the body that comes in waves, builds to a crescendo, and then every five or 10 minutes climbs to an even higher level.

"It goes on and on and you can't get comfortable, even with painkillers. And you get this feeling of impending doom, that something serious is about to go wrong.

"There's no two ways about it, if someone had given me a loaded gun I would have ended it there and then – it was horrific."

Jamie's symptoms continued for another 18 hours, with medical attention able to ease them very slightly but only time provided the cure.

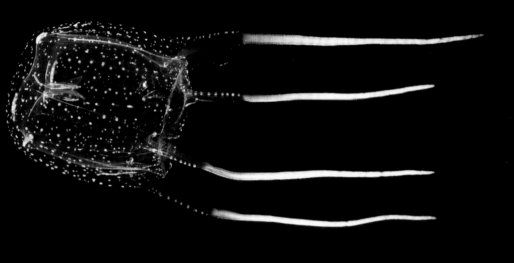

JIMBLE

FAMILY Carybdeidae

JIMBLE/LANTERN MEDUSA *Carybdea rastonii*
SOUTH-WESTERN STINGER *Carybdea xaymacana*

JELLIES

WITH A CUBE-SHAPED 3–5cm long bell, jimbles look like, but are not, Irukandji-type jellyfish. They have been reported mainly from South Australian and southern West Australian waters. They spend the majority of their time near the seabed and rise towards the surface only during the morning and evening and on cloudy days. Jimbles are more common in spring, and known to occur in swarms in sheltered waters such as bays and estuaries. They feed mostly on small fish, which are killed by their trailing tentacles and then digested in the bell.

Although not as much concern as Irukandji-type jellyfish, jimbles can cause a painful sting, especially for children. Symptoms of a jimble sting can be similar to, and may be more severe than, those caused by bluebottles or Indo-Pacific men-o'-war (see next page). The sting generally produces a raised white weal surrounded by red lines on the skin, and in some cases further complications have caused permanent scarring. On rare occasions a jimble sting will be as painful and serious as that of the sea wasp variants (see page 122) and further medical help may be required.

Physalia physalis

A bluebottle in
waters off NSW

BLUEBOTTLES

GENUS *Physalia*

ATLANTIC PORTUGUESE MAN-O'-WAR
Physalia physalis
INDO-PACIFIC PORTUGUESE MAN-O'-WAR
Physalia utriculus

ALTHOUGH OFTEN considered to be jellyfish, these creatures are not jellyfish. Although relatives of corals and jellyfish, they are hydrozoans. Each appears to be a single creature, but is actually a colony of four different types of smaller organisms – polyps – that can't survive independently. Each polyp type plays a different role in its colony – from the float, to the feeding tentacles, to those that are involved in reproduction or capturing prey.

The air-filled sac of an Atlantic Portuguese man-o'-war can be up to 8cm long. Each has a single long blue tentacle hanging underneath that can contract to a few centimetres, or extend to more than 1m. The Indo-Pacific man-o'-war has a larger sac (up to 14cm long) and multiple tentacles, which may each reach a length of 10m. The floating sac of a bluebottle has muscular fibres that, if contracted, will raise or shape it into a 'sail', allowing the colony to be blown across the water. Onshore winds can leave beaches littered with these creatures. Remarkably the sacs come in right- and left-handed varieties that sail in opposite directions, so a single blow can't wipe out an entire population.

Bluebottle tentacles are lined with stinging cells – nematocysts – that fire when they touch skin, causing immediate burning pain and usually long, raised weals with a prominent 'beading' effect.

Occasionally stings from the Indo-Pacific man-o'-war can cause Irukandji-like symptoms (see page 124) such as back pain, nausea, sweating and painful breathing. Although the stings of *Physalia* found in Australian waters cause pain, they're not usually life-threatening, unless a person has an acute allergy, which is very rare. If stung, use your fingers to pick off any tentacles sticking to skin: because the pads of the fingers are thick, no stinging occurs. But wash your hands thoroughly afterwards because any stinging cells remaining on the hands can sting thinner skin areas, such as eyes, lips and genital areas, if touched.

The best pain relief is hot water at 45°C for 20 minutes, which is available from special hot water showers on a few beaches (mainly in the Sydney area). Water hotter than 45°C can scald and blister the skin, and cooler water is much less effective. A cloth-wrapped icepack, or ice wrapped in a polythene bag, is the most convenient way to give fair pain relief, but pain usually takes some 15–20 minutes to fade. Seek medical aid if other symptoms develop.

JELLIES

FIRST ✚ AID

BLUEBOTTLE STING

GENERAL SYMPTOMS

The nematocysts (stinging cells) on bluebottle tentacles cause intense pain that may last from a few minutes to many hours. The reactions of people stung by a bluebottle varies, but children, people with allergies and asthmatics can be greatly distressed, and in some cases develop breathing difficulties.

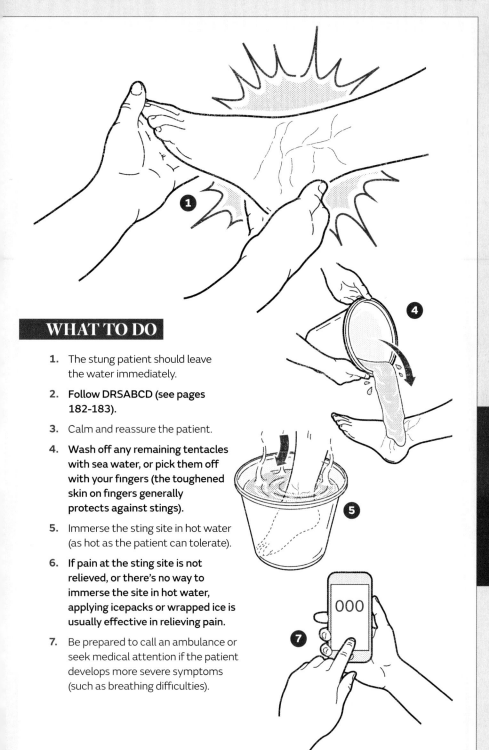

WHAT TO DO

1. The stung patient should leave the water immediately.

2. **Follow DRSABCD (see pages 182-183).**

3. Calm and reassure the patient.

4. **Wash off any remaining tentacles with sea water, or pick them off with your fingers (the toughened skin on fingers generally protects against stings).**

5. Immerse the sting site in hot water (as hot as the patient can tolerate).

6. **If pain at the sting site is not relieved, or there's no way to immerse the site in hot water, applying icepacks or wrapped ice is usually effective in relieving pain.**

7. Be prepared to call an ambulance or seek medical attention if the patient develops more severe symptoms (such as breathing difficulties).

FIRST AID

JELLIES

OTHER JELLYFISH, NETTLES AND SEA LICE

ORDERS Semaeostomeae, Rhizostomeae

MOON/ SAUCER JELLY *Aurelia aurita*
STINGING SEA NETTLE *Chrysaora quinquecirrha*
JELLY BLUBBER *Catostylus mosaicus*
LION'S MANE JELLYFISH *Cyanea capillata*
MAUVE STINGER *Pelagia noctiluca*

THERE ARE a number of jellyfish species of the orders Semaeostomeae and Rhizostomeae with nematocysts that can sting people, although no Australian fatalities have been attributed to them. The jelly blubber (*Catostylus mosaicus*) is the most commonly encountered species in Australian east-coast waters and can occur in great numbers. Its dome-shaped bell can grow to a diameter of 30cm or more and varies in colour depending on location and season. Off Sydney it's often creamy white to brown, but further north is blueish. Its thick trailing tentacles have nematocysts capable of inflicting stings, and these can be more potent during the breeding season but pose no serious risk to people.

The mauve stinger grows to about 10cm across the bell and has eight tentacles. It's believed to occur in ocean and coastal waters worldwide, including Australia. It can appear in massive swarms, especially in the Mediterranean Sea, where it's thought that up to 250,000 people have been stung in a single summer. There have been considerably fewer reports of it in Australian waters.

The lion's mane jellyfish (*Cyanea capillata*) – the largest known jellyfish species – has been reported from cold, high-latitude waters worldwide, including off Australia and New Zealand. Its umbrella-shaped bell can grow to more than 1m in diameter; its trailing tentacles up to 10m long. Its painful stings are not known to be fatal, and can be deactivated by vinegar.

The term 'sea-lice' is a catch-all that describes the many minor skin irritations that affect surfers, swimmers and divers worldwide. No single organism or phenomenon has been identified as the cause. Various minor jellyfish stings – including some possibly from the tentacles of dead animals broken up in surf with nematocysts still viable – have been implicated. So too have marine algae, larvae of various types and even small crustaceans.

Although stings from species in these groups often result in little more than mild irritation, some people may find them particularly painful and require first aid.

Cyanea capillata

A lion's mane jellyfish

Aurelia aurita

The moon jelly (*Aurelia aurita*) is a common sight in waters around the globe. It can measure up to 40cm in diameter and have stinging tentacles at each corner of its square shaped mouth. The edges of the jelly's mantle are also lined with stinging tentacles. They are often found in huge swarms, or blooms, as pictured here.

Butterfly cod

LOOK BUT BE CAREFUL ABOUT TOUCHING THE
BEAUTIFUL FISH IN THE WATERS AROUND OUR
CONTINENT: YOU CAN NEVER KNOW FOR SURE
WHICH COME EQUIPPED WITH POISONOUS SPINES.

VENOMOUS FISHES

VENOMOUS FISH deliver toxins through sharp spines used
for defence rather than attack. These may be concealed,
only becoming obvious when used, as is true of stonefish,
or displayed conspicuously as a warning, as with butterfly cod.
The venoms some of these fish possess are potentially lethal, while
others cause only localised reactions. Stings can occur even after a
fish has died.

As a general rule, fish that have been damaged, in a fishing net
for example, are less likely to deliver a sting, probably because the
envenomation system has already been triggered or damaged.
When a wound from a fish spine bleeds profusely it's also less likely
to cause intense symptoms, probably due to the flushing or dilution
of venom by the blood. Some fish spines aren't connected to venom
sacs and therefore produce few symptoms.

General symptoms of fish stings such as shock, respiratory
depression and death occur when the venom enters and disperses
through the body. The victim's body weight is a major factor in the
severity of the symptoms, meaning children are usually at greater
risk than adults. The physical health of the victim is also relevant,
and conditions such as asthma and coronary artery disease may
increase the chance that a sting will be fatal.

Other fish produce cutting injuries with knife-like spines that
may or may not result in envenomation. In many cases, a slime
exists on the spines that may contribute as greatly to inflammation
and infections as any venom.

The site of the wound, the number of punctures and their
pattern will help identify the fish that caused the injury.
Fortunately, there is generally little variation in the symptoms of
various fish stings, although the severity may vary greatly, both
between and within species.

Synanceia verrucosa

STONEFISHES

FAMILY Scorpaenidae

REEF STONEFISH *Synanceia verrucosa*
ESTUARINE STONEFISH *Synanceia horrida*

THERE ARE TWO SPECIES of stonefish found in Australian waters, mainly in tropical parts. Stonefish venom is among the most potent of all fish venoms and several deaths have been attributed to it. Stonefish usually grow to about 35cm and are superbly camouflaged. They're entirely covered by loose grey or brown skin and look remarkably like substrate rocks, or lumps of coral. They're easy to recognise in the water column because of their squat bodies and ungainly swimming style, although open-water sightings are rare.

They generally live on rubble- or coral-strewn bottoms, although they'll occasionally use their large pectoral fins to bury into sand or mud. They're sometimes stranded on reefs at low tide – making them a great danger to reef-walkers – and can survive for many hours out of water.

Stonefish rely on immobility and camouflage to survive: they're ambush predators and generally won't reveal themselves by swimming away if they're disturbed. Instead, they erect their 13 venomous dorsal spines, which are strong enough to penetrate rubber-soled shoes.

Those stung experience immediate and often severe pain around the sting site, which rapidly increases in intensity but – in the case of 'average' stings – usually lessens over the following hours. Immersing the wound in hot water throughout the time that the victim is in pain is the recommended first aid. In cases of severe stonefish envenomation prompt medical treatment is essential. Victims may develop breathing difficulties and heart failure.

Reef stonefish

Pterois volitans

Butterfly cod

SCORPION-FISHES

FAMILY Scorpaenidae

OCELLATED (LONGFIN) WASPFISH *Apistus carinatus*
FORTESCUE *Centropogon australis*
BULLROUT *Notesthes robusta*
BUTTERFLY COD, OR RED LIONFISH *Pterois volitans*
SPOTTED SCORPIONFISH *Scorpaena plumieri*
DEMON STINGER *Inimicus didactylus*
DEVIL SCORPIONFISH, OR
FALSE STONEFISH *Scorpaenopsis diabolus*

THIS MOSTLY marine fish family includes a large number of highly venomous species. Worldwide, there are about 350 members of the family Scorpaenidae, about 80 of which have been recorded in Australian waters. Species vary considerably in size, but most have compact bodies liberally decorated with spined fins. Dorsal, anal and pelvic spines have venom glands attached. Scorpionfish colours tend to match their environment, and vary from species to species. Tropical species found among corals tend to be colourful, while those from sheltered temperate waters are often dull and brown.

Species known as butterfly cod – particularly *Pterois volitans* and *P. antennata* – are probably the scorpionfish best known to Australians. These strikingly beautiful fish, characterised by extended spine arrays like Native American headdresses, grow to about 30cm and are frequently seen in tropical and subtropical waters. They sometimes swim nose-down, so their 13 dorsal spines are projecting forwards. They seem unafraid of divers and it's usually fine to swim with them provided you stay well clear of their spines.

In contrast are devilfish species, which are close relatives to true stonefishes. Also known as demon stinger, bearded ghoul, goblinfish and stingfish, species such as *Inimicus caledonicus* and *I. didactylus* grow to about 25cm and typically live on the sea floor, where they wait, well camouflaged for prey. They usually inhabit deep water offshore, but are also found in shallower, muddy waters such as mangrove swamps. There are reports of them attacking underwater photographers and they are a painful nuisance for recreational and commercial fishers.

Scorpionfish stings aren't known to be fatal but many victims report extreme pain. Other symptoms include headaches, vomiting and breathing difficulties. It's wise to follow first aid with medical treatment as soon as possible.

For first aid treatment, see page 185.

FISHES

Plotosus spp.

CATFISHES

FAMILIES Plotosidae, Ariidae

CNIDOGLANIS spp., PLOTOSUS spp.,
TACHYSURUS spp., NETUMA spp.

Striped eel catfish

K NOWN BY a variety of common names –
including sea barbel, striped catfish, eel-tailed
catfish, cobbler and cattie – these fishes are
found in the coastal or inland waters of every
continent except Antarctica. About 40 species are
known in Australia.

They lack scales and vary greatly in length, with
marine species ranging in size from about 5cm to 1m.
Catfishes get their common name from the whisker-like
sensory appendages, called barbels, that protrude from
around their mouths. These are used to locate food in
underwater substrates in ocean or freshwater
environments and although they may look threatening,
they aren't dangerous.

It's wise, however, to handle all catfishes with care
because they have barbed, serrated spines on their dorsal
and pectoral fins. These are usually protected by a thin
covering and capable of puncturing skin on contact.
Not all catfish spines are venomous, but those that are
have a gland at the base of the spine from which venom
flows. One of the most venomous is the striped eel
catfish (*Plotosus lineatus*), the only species found on coral
reefs. It's often seen by divers and is best left alone,
although juveniles have an unmistakeable habit of
schooling in intense balls that are mesmerising to
witness. Even in non-venomous species there's the
danger of a spine breaking off in a wound. Pulling it out
can cause more damage, so it's best to seek medical help.

For first aid treatment, see page 185.

Schooling striped catfish. These catfish can grow to 35cm in length and school in shoals of about 100 fish. They are chiefly a tropical fish but are seen as far south as Sydney and Esperance. The dorsal and pectoral fins have hidden spines that can inflict severe pain.

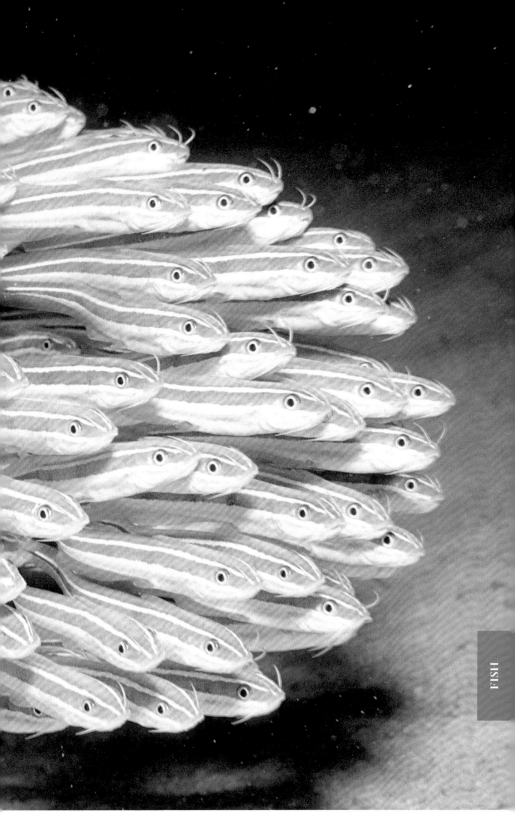

OTHER
VENOMOUS
FISHES

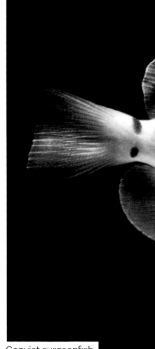

Acanthurus dussumieri

SURGEONFISH &
UNICORNFISH

FAMILY Acanthuridae

EYESTRIPE SURGEONFISH
Acanthurus dussumieri
CONVICT SURGEONFISH
Acanthurus triostegus

Convict surgeonfish

Kathetostoma
nigrofasciatum

STARGAZER

FAMILY Uranoscopidae

DEEPWATER STARGAZER
Kathetostoma nigrofasciatum
FRINGED STARGAZER
Ichthyscopus barbatus

Siganus lineatus

RABBITFISH

FAMILY Siganidae

**GOLDEN-LINED
SPINEFOOT**
Siganus lineatus
MARBLED SPINEFOOT
Siganus rivulatus

Halophryne diemensis

FROGFISH

FAMILY Batrachoididae

BANDED FROGFISH
Halophryne diemensis
Batrachoides spp.

Enoplosus armatus

OLD WIFE

FAMILY Enoplosidae

BASTARD DORY
Enoplosus armatus

WHETHER VENOMOUS or not, many fish species have sharp spines – often in or near their fins – that can cause puncture wounds or lacerations, so it's worth handling any fish with caution. Wounds aside, there's enough uncertainty about which species have venomous spines and which don't.

Different species bear their spines in different positions. They're very sharp and in the dorsal array, for example, in the old wife – a species commonly encountered by divers and well known for its striped markings. Its spines are generally described as venomous, but some divers report that wounds from them cause little pain.

Rabbitfish are decorated with 24 spines – distributed among dorsal, pelvic and anal fins – and all have venom glands attached. Surgeonfish and unicornfish are usually colourful and also widely encountered by divers. The name surgeonfish comes from the scalpel-like spines on either side of the tail – dangerously sharp and often marked by bright warning colours. Surgeonfish

Old wife

spines haven't been confirmed as venomous, but are thought to be.

Most people injured by these families and species are anglers who've caught an individual on a line or in a net – good reason to have a pair of gloves as part of your fishing kit.

Fish spines also cause injuries among swimmers and reef-walkers who accidentally step on one of the well-camouflaged, bottom-dwelling species, such as the stargazer. The stargazer's eyes are on the flat top surface of its square head, which allows it to spend a good deal of time hidden in bottom mud. Its venom glands are linked to grooves in its two shoulder spines, which protrude through a skin-sheath on either side of its body. To add to the fun, some stargazers can also release an electric discharge that's similar to an electric ray's (see page 165).

The frogfish most often live under rock ledges and inhabit rubble such as stones and coral, but they qualify as bottom-dwellers because of their habit of swimming over mudflats. They have hollow spines on their dorsal fin and gill

covers that are connected to venom glands. They grow to about 25cm, are scaleless and are able to survive long periods out of water.

Injuries from the spines and venom of these species are at worst painful. There are reports that pain may be less severe if the wound bleeds freely because it's thought that whatever venom is injected is washed out by blood.

For first aid treatment, see page 185.

Golden-lined spinefoot

FISH

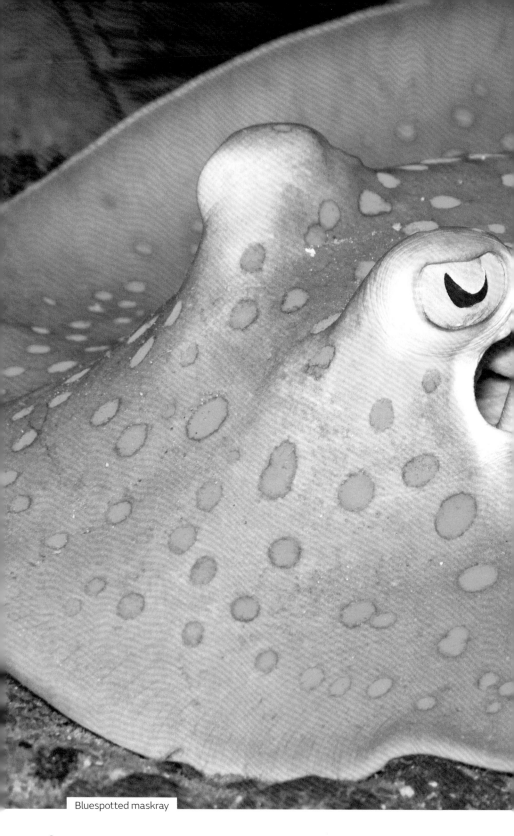

Bluespotted maskray

DANGEROUS MARINE ANIMALS

AN ARRAY OF fascinating venomous, stinging or irritating organisms rounds out this marine section of dangerous Australian creatures, including stingrays and sea snakes. Although the latter are closely related to land snakes and highly venomous, they usually have small fangs and are not equipped with venom-delivery systems as effective as their terrestrial counterparts.

None of the creatures listed here are aggressive and all will only attack if harassed. Some, however, are extremely venomous animals that are known to have caused deaths. This includes blue-ringed octopuses and cone snails. For both, the danger is amplified because of their appeal to people due to their attractive appearance, and habit of sometimes being within reach of low-tide reef- or rock-platform-walkers.

Sponges, among the simplest of multicellular organisms, are included here because of the severe reactions that contact can induce when human skin is exposed to their spicules (tiny skeletal elements) and the toxic slime some produce.

A SINGLE CONE SNAIL STING CARRIES ENOUGH TOXIN TO KILL **10 HEALTHY ADULTS**

ENOUGH TOXIN TO KILL
10
ADULTS

OTHER SEA CREATURES

BLUE-RINGED OCTOPUS

GENUS *Hapalochlaena*

GREATER BLUE-RINGED OCTOPUS
Hapalochlaena lunulata
SOUTHERN BLUE-RINGED OCTOPUS
Hapalochlaena maculosa
BLUE-LINED OCTOPUS *Hapalochlaena fasciata*

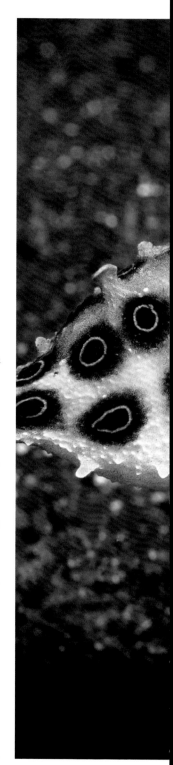

ALTHOUGH NO bigger than an outstretched hand, and small enough to hide in an empty shell, just one blue-ringed octopus contains enough venom to paralyse 10 people. These creatures usually hide in rock pools and coral reefs, but are often encountered when stranded after big tides along rocky coastlines.

These deadly creatures can be found right around Australia's coastline but are more commonly encountered in northern Western Australia, southern New South Wales and South Australia. They are masters of camouflage and it's normally difficult to spot their yellowish coloured bodies with dark blotches in which there are blue or purple circles or lines. But if they are disturbed or threatened the blue markings begin to pulse, warning potential predators to stay away.

This phenomenon can attract children and inquisitive beachcombers, who have been known to have been bitten when they've picked up or handled the creatures, either deliberately or accidentally.

Blue-ringed octopuses – known as the world's most lethal – inject venom through the 'beaks' at the base of their tentacles. The bite is virtually painless and often goes unnoticed. But within as little as 10 minutes a victim can be fighting for their life. Neurotoxins in the venom can result in vomiting, breathing difficulties, heart failure, paralysis and blindness.

Deaths usually result from respiratory failure. Victims can be saved if they are given immediate mouth-to-mouth resuscitation (see page 182) and then put on a ventilator in hospital until the toxins clear from the body.

Hapalochlaena fasciata

Blue-lined octopus

Geographer cone snails. Considered to be the most venomous of the family, geographer cone snails can grow to about 15cm and are indigenous to the reefs of the Indo-Pacific.

Conus geographus

CONE SHELLS

FAMILY Conidae

CAT CONE *Conus catus*
GEOGRAPHER (GEOGRAPHY) CONE SNAIL
Conus geographus
STRIATED CONE *Conus striatus*
TULIP CONE *Conus tulipa*
TEXTILE (CLOTH) OF GOLD CONE *Conus textile*

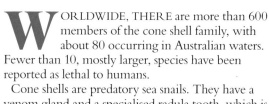

WORLDWIDE, THERE are more than 600 members of the cone shell family, with about 80 occurring in Australian waters. Fewer than 10, mostly larger, species have been reported as lethal to humans.

Cone shells are predatory sea snails. They have a venom gland and a specialised radula tooth, which is propelled from an extendable proboscis, which they use to attack and paralyse prey. The radula is often compared to a dart, or harpoon. The prey of smaller cone shells are primarily marine worms. Large species consume bottom-dwelling fish, and, because they don't want prey to swim away to die, their venom is considerably more toxic.

Once injected, cone shell venom acts rapidly. Symptoms of a serious sting include intense pain at the site and associated swelling, numbness and tingling, as well as nausea and vomiting. The symptoms may be immediate or delayed for days. Death – which occurs in about 25 per cent of cases – is usually a result of muscle paralysis and respiratory failure. Knowing the difference between relatively benign cones and deadly ones requires expert understanding. The safest measure is to not handle any live specimens. There are no antivenoms available for any cone shell species.

Interestingly, cone shell venom is showing great promise as a source of new pain-killing drugs. Some of its core compounds include proteins that target certain human pain receptors. Research indicates these particular proteins may be many thousands of times more potent than morphine, and without its addictive and other side effects.

OTHER SEA CREATURES

Aipysurus laevis

Olive sea snake

SEA SNAKES

FAMILY Elapidae SUBFAMILY Hydrophiinae

BEAKED SEA SNAKE *Enhydrina schistosa*
OLIVE SEA SNAKE *Aipysurus laevis*
STOKES' SEA SNAKE *Astrotia stokesii*
YELLOW-BELLIED SEA SNAKE *Pelamis platurus*

MORE THAN 60 SPECIES of sea snake have been described, mostly in the Western Pacific and Indian Oceans. They are air-breathing reptiles and closely related to the front-fanged land snakes that inhabit Australia. The main feature that sets sea snakes apart is a flattened, paddle-like tail for swimming. Some species live entirely at sea; some come ashore to lay eggs. Most grow to about 120–150cm.

All sea snakes have venom glands and fangs and some species have very potent venom. However, some don't use venom for prey capture, most are reluctant to bite humans and some are so docile they're considered no danger to humans. Sea snakes are known to approach divers, probably out of curiosity, but cases of them biting without provocation are very rare. The olive and Stokes' sea snakes are among species reported as more aggressive. The yellow-bellied sea snake is likely to bite only when provoked because it uses its venom mainly for self-defence, gulping prey without an envenoming bite. Most recorded bites have come from sea snakes being caught in fishing nets or handled.

Sea snake fangs are small and their venom delivery to humans is inefficient. These snakes are also renowned for 'dry bites': like terrestrial snakes, they can control how much venom they inject in a bite and in many cases don't inject any at all. The best advice is to observe sea snakes from a distance and never handle them.

Bites that include envenomation are often barely noticed and painless at first, although they may occasionally leave wounds and result in blood loss. Symptoms usually present within two hours, and may include muscle weakness that develops into paralysis, breathing difficulties and sometimes heart failure. If envenomation is suspected, emergency medical treatment is vital.

OTHER SEA CREATURES

STINGING HYDROIDS

FAMILY Plumulariidae

CYPRESS SEA FERN *Aglaophenia cupressina*
WHITE STINGING SEA FERN
Lytocarpus philippinus

THESE ARE colonial animals that grow in clumps, attached to submerged rocks or reefs, and tend to look a lot like ferns or feathery seaweed. They're often found in places with a current because this carries plankton prey past their 'fronds', which are lined with stinging polyps designed to capture this prey.

Even a slight brush by a person against a stinging hydroid can produce rapid pain from a sting, although the effects seem to be variable. At times divers appear to be able to handle hydroids without being stung.

Conversely, the pain from a sting can be quite intense, with skin around the site going red and weals developing, with reports suggesting that healing may take up to a month in some cases. Generally, it's better not to touch any hydroid, because of the unknown potential for a painful sting. For first aid, see page 185.

Aglaophenia cupressina

Cypress sea fern

BIGGEST DANGERS IN AUSTRALIAN WATERS

THE ANIMALS ON THE LIST opposite were distilled from *The top 30 dangerous animals in Australia*, first published on *australiangeographic.com.au*. The top 30 list was developed by staff of the Australian Museum, Sydney, who rated animals out of 10 based on the threat they pose to human life, combined with the likelihood of encountering them. We have ranked the sea creatures in that original list from 1 to 10. See also *Biggest dangers on Australian land* on page 80.

Box jellyfish

100   0

HIGHLY DANGEROUS   **LESS DANGEROUS**

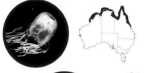

1. Box jellyfish (*Chironex fleckeri*)

2. Irukandji (*Carukia barnesi*, and others)

3. Bull shark (*Carcharhinus leucas*)

4. Saltwater or estuarine crocodile (*Crocodylus porosus*)

5. Blue-ringed octopus (Genus *Hapalochlaena*)

TOP 10 MOST DANGEROUS MARINE CREATURES IN AUSTRALIAN WATERS

6. Cone shells (*Conus* spp.)

7. Tiger shark (*Galeocerdo cuvier*)

8. Great white shark (*Carcharodon carcharias*)

9. Yellow-bellied sea snake (*Pelamis platurus*)

10. Bluebottle (*Physalia physalis*)

OTHER SEA CREATURES

Millepora platyphylla

Blade fire coral

FIRE CORALS

CLASS Hydrozoa

BLADE FIRE CORAL *Millepora platyphylla*

IN SPITE OF THEIR NAME, these colonial animals are actually hydrozoans – they're related to both corals and jellyfish, but are not true corals. Their similarity with corals is enhanced because they create hard, coral-like skeletons and play an important role in reef-building. They're highly variable in size, shape and colour but have in common a calcareous skeleton covered with very small pores, from which protrude the tentacles of individual animals. The pores are the source of fire corals' generic name *Millepora*.

The tentacles have nematocysts (specialist stinging cells) that are used to stun prey, and many divers and snorkellers in tropical waters have had the painful experience of accidentally brushing against them. They're not particularly toxic, but can inflict quite intense local pain. Stinging or burning is usually felt in 5–30 minutes, followed by the appearance of a rash and associated itching. Some lymph gland swelling may occur, and more rarely nausea and vomiting. Vinegar is suggested to reduce pain, and soaking the sting site in hot water, or applying heat packs, can relieve symptoms.

If the sting also involves a coral cut, ensure the site is cleaned with soap and water as soon as possible and then flushed repeatedly with fresh water. Rinse the cut daily and, ideally, apply an antibiotic ointment. If an infection develops, seek medical advice because marine infections can be particularly hard to control.

OTHER SEA CREATURES

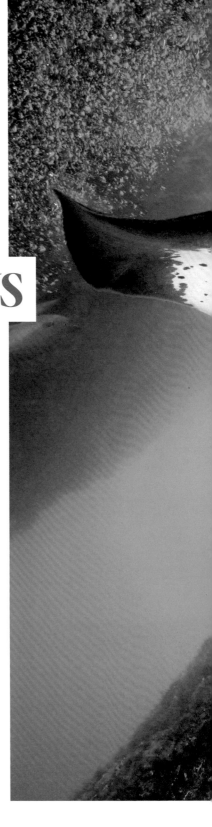

STINGRAYS

FAMILIES Dasyatididae, Gymnuridae,
Myliobatidae, Urolophidae

SMOOTH STINGRAY *Dasyatis brevicaudata*
ESTUARY STINGRAY/STINGAREE
Dasyatis fluviorum
BLUESPOTTED MASKRAY *Neotrygon kuhlii*
BLOTCHED FANTAIL RAY *Taeniura meyeni*
PORCUPINE RAY *Urogymnus asperrimus*

DEATHS CAUSED BY stingrays are extremely rare. But since the 2006 fatal wounding of wildlife advocate Steve Irwin by a large stingray, these creatures have come to be feared far more than they need be. Steve was injured while snorkelling and shooting a documentary at Batt Reef, off Port Douglas, in the Great Barrier Reef. Rays are fish that are related to sharks. Many have one or more spines at the base of the tail, but these are used only for self-defence. Stingrays are, otherwise, gentle creatures, known to be interested in, and occasionally swimming with, snorkellers and divers. They are usually highly unlikely to strike, unless provoked – either accidentally or deliberately.

In Australian waters, rays vary in size from the smooth stingray, which can grow to 2m wide, to species less than 50cm wide. Many species inhabit shallow waters and feed on bottom-dwelling prey, lying covered by substrate with only their eyes or

Dasyatis brevicaudata

Smooth stingray

Bluespotted maskray

part of their tail visible. They are often first spotted as they swim away. These fish can by trodden on by unwary waders and painful jabs to feet and ankles are the most widely known injuries. The bony spine can easily penetrate soft shoes as well as skin.

Venom can be injected into a wound but the spine's serrated edges are often the biggest problem, capable of causing serious lacerations and known to have inflicted a lethal injury on at least one occasion. Parts of the spine may also break off in a wound, or deposit organisms or a toxic slime that may inflame wounds and lead to further infections. Because of this it's not unusual for apparently minor stingray stabs to take months to heal.

For first aid treatment, see page 185.

STINGRAY SPINES, which are located at the base of the tail, have serrated edges and it's these that often do the most damage. Many rays also have a venom gland at the base of the spine and although the venom is usually painful it is rarely fatal.

A shocking truth

Some rays can deliver a blast of electricity
strong enough to knock over a person.

ELECTRIC RAYS – also known as numb rays, numbfish and torpedo fish – have modified muscle cells that can produce electricity used for navigation, stunning prey or protection from predators. On rare occasions, a person can be struck and temporarily disabled, putting them at risk of drowning. In such cases, CPR may be needed (see pages 182–183).

The special cells – electrocytes – are disk-like and usually stacked in a ray's two electric organs. Having them arranged in this way – like a bank of batteries – increases their electrical output. The organs have about 45 stacks, each containing several hundred or more electrocytes.

Situated on either side of the spine near the head or tail, depending on the species, the electric organs are controlled by four central nerves that come from each side of a specialised brain lobe. The main nerves branch repeatedly, then attach to the lower side of each cell in an electrocyte stack.

Changes in ion concentration in individual electrocytes generate electrical charges in small amounts, and a group of special nerve cells called the pacemaker nucleus is engaged to discharge all the individual charges simultaneously. The electric blast created varies from 8 to 220 volts, and is passed from the electrically negative underside of the ray to its positive topside.

SEGMENTED OR BRISTLE WORMS

CLASS Polychaeta

GOLDEN FIREWORM *Chloeia flava*
BRISTLE WORM *Eurythoe complanata*
BITING REEF WORM *Eunice aphroditois*
SOUTHERN SEAMOUSE *Aphrodita australis*

THESE ARE worms with body segments that have bristly protrusions called chaetae, hence the common name 'bristle worms'. They are common and widespread, inhabiting oceans at all depths and temperatures.

The form and colour of these worms vary greatly, and they range in size from about 10cm to as long as 3m. Their bristles are made of chitin, a polymer related to cellulose that's found, among other places, in the skeletons of crustaceans and insects. These bristles can cause injury when they contact the skin and in some species, such as the fireworms, are venomous

The biting reef worm is arguably the nightmare species of this group. It can grow to more than 1.5m in length and buries itself in the sea floor awaiting prey, which it attacks with great speed and ferocity. It can inflict savage wounds on people, but fortunately most bites are rarely more than a few millimetres wide and infection is the main concern.

Bristle worm spines break off easily in skin and are hard to see. Often a rash or irritation is the only sign. Aquarists suggest using masking or duct tape to remove bristles. If the spines are venomous, additional symptoms include intense itching or burning that may last a week; sometimes associated with blisters and a rash.

The symptoms are generally worse in the first three days, but can recur, and local numbness can endure for weeks. The site often becomes swollen and inflamed. If symptoms persist for more than a few days it's wise to seek medical treatment.

Chlocia flava

Golden fireworm

SPONGES

PHYLUM Porifera

Neofibularia irata, Neofibularia mordens, Lissodendoryx spp.

MORE THAN 8500 species of sponge have so far been described worldwide but they are a poorly understood group. Sponges are the most basic multi-celled animals. They live attached to reefs, rocks and the sea floor and lack the more complex digestive, circulatory and nervous systems of other animals. Instead they rely on water flow through their porous bodies for their food, oxygen and waste-disposal needs.

Different species are hard to distinguish from one another but the mineral structures called spicules that help strengthen their body walls – sponge 'skeletons' – are comonly used in identification. Spicules are made either of calcium carbonate or silica and it's believed they may play a role in skin irritations caused by contact with sponges. A small number of species have also developed toxins and distasteful or irritating coatings as defence mechanisms: an example is *Neofibularia irata*, found in Great Barrier Reef waters.

The main effect of sponge contact is skin irritation, usually felt in minutes to a few hours and often exacerbated if the area is rubbed. Symptoms may worsen during 24 or more hours and the area can take a week or more to return to normal. Occasionally a type of dermatitis known as cheiropompholyx, or dyshidrotic eczema, develops.

A variety of sponges

169

Octopus vulgaris

Common octopus

COMMON OCTOPUSES

CLASS Cephalopoda

COMMON OCTOPUS *Octopus vulgaris*

OCTOPUSES ARE mostly placid creatures of surprising intellect. They're believed to be among the smartest invertebrates – that wide group of phyla in which octopuses are most closely related to squid and cuttlefish. Octopuses are reported to have used tools, boarded fishing boats and opened holds to find food.

These eight-armed molluscs are found in all waters from the poles to the tropics. About 300 species have been described, in habitats as diverse as near-shore ledges and pools to open-ocean depths of 5000m. The regularly encountered common octopus occurs worldwide in tropical and temperate waters. Large individuals may have an arm span of more than 1m and weigh 10kg, but most are smaller than that. The largest known species of octopus, the giant Pacific octopus (*Enteroctopus dofleini*) found in the temperate north Pacific, is commonly 5m across and weighs 50kg.

Octopuses eat a range of prey from worms and prawns to fish. Because some disable prey with a venom produced in the salivary glands, which can be injected through a bite, they should be approached with care.

Octopuses prefer rocky ledges and overhangs so are of little risk to beach swimmers, but can be encountered by divers or snorkellers. Reports of octopuses biting humans in the water are rare, and it's thought such occurrences are in response to attacks with a fishing-spear or knife. A puncture wound usually marks the site and symptoms, including localised pain, swelling and a spreading 'fiery' pain, often follow. These reportedly diminish if wounds are flushed with hot water, but can take days to disappear completely, and may become itchy.

For first aid treatment, see page 185.

OTHER SEA CREATURES

Gymnothorax javanicus

Giant moray

EELS

FAMILIES Muraenidae, Congridae

GIANT MORAY *Gymnothorax javanicus*
WHITEMOUTH MORAY *Gymnothorax meleagris*
SOUTHERN CONGER *Conger verreauxi*

THE FEARSOME reputation of some larger eels – conger species in particular – isn't entirely without merit. However, it is not so well deserved by the moray eels, which tend to look more dangerous than they really are.

The habit of morays of lying still with mouths agape and impressively pointy teeth on display is mostly their way of getting water to pass over their gills, allowing them to breathe. But this also contributes to a rather fearsome and intimidating appearance that belies a normally shy disposition.

Morays are carnivores that prey on a variety of marine animals including other fishes, crustaceans and octopuses. They are common reef inhabitants but are mostly nocturnal, so divers usually only see their heads poking from crevices and holes. They have a remarkable second set of jaws – pharyngeal jaws – concealed in their throats. When morays feed, these jaws extend into their mouths to pull snared prey back into their throats.

In general, morays would rather hide or flee than fight a creature the size of a human. They've been known to attack if their burrow has been disturbed, and have also bitten divers attempting to hand-feed them – possibly because their poor vision hasn't allowed them to separate the food from the fingers holding it. And they've been known to get stroppy with divers if they're used to being fed regularly but food isn't offered. Thankfully, the practice of hand-feeding morays appears to be on the decline, and is even banned in some places.

On the other hand, conger eels have a well-deserved reputation for possessing a vicious disposition. They are aggressive predators that can grow to an impressive size – up to 3m in length and a weight of 40kg – and have been known to attack humans.

Species in Australian waters mostly grow to a maximum of 1m or so, and usually only weigh 1–10kg.

Eel bite wounds tend to be ragged and torn and secondary infection is common. They generally result in blood loss, sometimes profuse. In cases where blood loss is severe enough, victims can go into shock.

Eels can sometimes be mistaken for sea snakes, which can be readily distinguished by their scales (as opposed to seemingly smooth scale-less skin) and flattened tails shaped like paddles.

OTHER SEA CREATURES

Epinephelus lanceolatus

Giant Queensland groper

GROPERS

FAMILY Serranidae

GIANT QUEENSLAND GROPER/COD
Epinephelus lanceolatus
SPOTTED COD *Plectropomus maculatus*
SOUTHERN AUSTRALIAN BASS
GROPER *Polyprion moeone*

THE QUEENSLAND groper is one of the world's largest bony fishes, and the largest known to dwell on coral reefs. It can grow to nearly 3m in length and weigh more than 400kg. Other species aren't as big, but share the traits of being curious and becoming accustomed to humans, especially if they're fed. If they learn that divers will bring food, they'll often stay in the same area and approach all divers. Given the size of gropers, this can be quite confronting for those experiencing it for the first time.

Smaller fish swallowed whole make up much of a groper's diet; their mouths have bands of small pointed teeth that are effective for holding prey rather than tearing it apart. It's thought that waving hands and feet may look 'fishy' in appearance and attract a groper's attention: many minor groper-related injuries are on hands or feet that have been spat out when fish realise they can't swallow them.

There are reports of unprovoked attacks and of deaths, although few are documented to a certainty. Stories persist: gropers are believed to be short-sighted and one frightening but funny tale concerns a Navy salvage diver, whose bright and shiny diving helmet was grabbed by a large groper, which then swam away, taking the wearer with it! Fortunately he was rescued by fellow divers, preventing a more serious incident.

The result of a groper bite is usually grazing and flesh tearing, sometimes deep, caused by the teeth. Profuse local bleeding can occur from the exposed tissues, but secondary infection is the greatest risk. Victims of a serious attack should also be monitored for shock.

For first aid treatment, see page 185.

OTHER SEA CREATURES

Actinodendron sp.

SEA ANEMONES

CLASS Anthozoa

HELL'S FIRE ANEMONE *Actinodendron arboreum*, and others including species of *Adamsia, Anemonia, Calliactis, Lebrunia, Physobrachia* and *Sagartia*.

MORE THAN 1000 species of sea anemone inhabit Earth's oceans. They are often brightly coloured and range in size from just a few centimetres to nearly 2m wide. The largest and brightest are found in tropical waters near the coast.

Anemones are related to jellyfish and corals. Some are free-floating but most attach to rocks or coral reefs, where their venomous tentacles wave in the current, waiting to ensnare passing prey, usually small fish. With the lightest touch the tentacles fire dart-like structures that inject a toxin, paralysing the prey.

This is then guided by the tentacles into the anemone's mouth.

Beachcombers and children are often drawn to the bright colours of anemones, near-shore specimens of which are often partially exposed at low tide. Brushes with them produce similar symptoms to minor jellyfish stings, and usually fade over minutes to hours.

It's important not to rub or scratch the sting site because it may intensify the sting, sometimes turning it into a slightly raised red blotch.

For first aid treatment, see page 185.

Mantis shrimp

Fastest claws in the sea

ALTHOUGH THEIR impact on humans is limited, mantis shrimps are sea creatures that definitely need to be handled with care.

Mantis shrimps are aggressive predatory crustaceans of the order Stomatopoda. About 150 species are known to inhabit Australian waters; most of which grow to a modest 10cm or so in length. What sets them apart is their manner of capturing prey.

They have large raptorial claws that closely resemble those of mantid insects – hence mantis shrimp. Species fall into two groups – 'spearers' and 'smashers'. The spearers' claws have a barbed tip used to stab and hold prey. The smashers' claws are more like a club, which they use to stun prey and smash them apart.

Both types strike by unfolding and swinging their claws forward with tremendous speed – and, in the case of smashers, terrifying power. Scientists have concluded that they accelerate their claws at 102,000m/s (367,200 km/h) and strike prey with forces of about 1500 Newtons.

Their claws move so fast that the collapsing cavitation bubbles immediately behind them produce a shock wave that may itself be enough to stun or kill prey.

Mantis shrimps have acquired the nickname 'prawn killers' in Australia, and are sometimes known as 'thumb splitters' in the USA. According to reports, larger individuals kept in aquariums have also been known to shatter their enclosing glass – apparently either when attacking their own reflection, or in response to a teasing finger waved at them from outside the aquarium.

SEA URCHINS
CLASS Echinoidea

SPINY SEA URCHIN *Centrostephanus rodgersii*
LONG-SPINED (BLACK) SEA URCHIN
Diadema setosum
LONG-SPINED SEA URCHIN *Diadema savignyi*
BANDED (DOUBLE-SPINED)
SEA URCHIN *Echinothrix calamaris*
DIADEMA (BLUE-BLACK) SEA URCHIN
Echinothrix diadema
FIRE URCHIN *Asthenosoma varium*
TAM O'SHANTER URCHIN *Araeosoma ijimai*
FLOWER URCHIN *Toxopneustes pileolus*
COLLECTOR URCHIN *Tripneustes gratilla*
PURPLE SEA URCHIN *Heliocidaris erythrogramma*
CROWN-OF-THORNS STARFISH *Acanthaster planci*

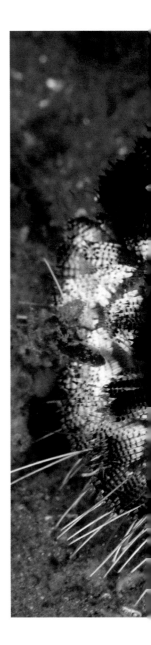

S EA URCHINS are slow-moving bottom grazers of mostly algae. There are more than 900 species worldwide, fewer than 10 per cent of which are of concern to humans. Sea urchins are echinoderms, the same group that contains sea stars and sea cucumbers: the name comes from the Ancient Greek for 'hedgehog skin'. They are a variety of sizes and colours with spines that may be stubby and blunt or long and sharp.

Long-spined varieties cause the most common problem: a spine penetrating and breaking off in a victim's skin. The spines of some species disappear in a few days, but others – such as *Ecinothrix* spp. – have venomous spines that can remain in the skin for months and emerge at a location in the body some distance from the original wound. *Asthenosoma* sp. spines are tipped with venom glands and inflict painful stings that can endure for hours. The best defence is to not handle urchins and wear tough-soled shoes when reef-walking.

Many echinoderms also have tiny, claw-like structures called pedicellariae scattered over the body. These are poorly understood but thought to keep the animal free of encrusting organisms. The flower urchin, which is regarded as the world's most dangerous urchin, has short spines that are almost impossible to detect among flower-like, venomous pedicellariae that snap shut and inject venom if disturbed. Flower urchin stings cause severe pain and can lead to paralysis and breathing difficulties. Deaths from pedicellariae envenomation have been reported.

For first aid treatment, see page 185.

Asthenosoma varium

Fire urchin

FIRST AID

BASIC FIRST AID

IN CASE OF EMERGENCY DIAL
TRIPLE ZERO (000)

The importance of knowing and understanding basic first aid can't be overstated. Some of the dangerous creatures described in this book are found in or near Australian population centres, and some inhabit our largest urban areas. A great many of the encounters that humans have with them are accidental, in which case a knowledge of first aid could well save a life.

The first aid response to some envenomations or injuries included in this book appear at or near the appropriate species entries. For instance, first aid for snakebite is in the snakes section. The following pages in this section cover the basic principles of first aid, as well as first aid for some of the issues that can arise from stings or bites, such as how to deal with bleeding, anaphylaxis and shock.

All first aid information in the book has been supplied by Australian Red Cross first aid and is published with their kind permission. The information presented is necessarily brief and not the equal of first aid training from a qualified instructor. For information about Australian Red Cross first aid courses, kits and equipment, telephone 1300 367 428 or visit *redcross.org.au*

BASIC FIRST AID KIT

A basic first aid kit should contain:
- A variety of plasters in different shapes and sizes
- Sterile gauze dressings
- Clean rolled bandages
- Disposable latex gloves
- Tweezers
- Scissors
- Safety pins

DRSABCD ACTION PLAN

IN CASE OF EMERGENCY DIAL TRIPLE ZERO (000)

WHAT TO DO

D
DANGER

Ensure the area is safe for yourself, others and the patient

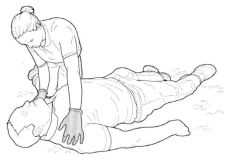

R
RESPONSE

Check for response
Ask name, squeeze shoulders

No response
Send for help, check for injuries, monitor response

No response
Make comfortable

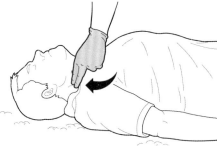

S
SEND FOR HELP

Call triple zero (000) for an ambulance or ask another person to make the call

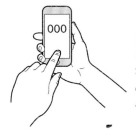

ACTION PLAN

FIRST AID

A

AIRWAY

Open mouth
If foreign material is present:
- place in the recovery position
- clear airway with fingers
- open airway by tilting head with chin lift

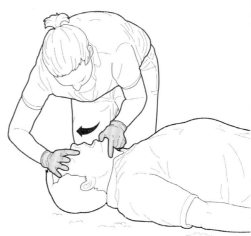

B

BREATHING

Check for breathing
Look, listen and feel

Not normal breathing
Start CPR, monitor breathing, manage injuries, treat for shock

Normal breathing
Place in recovery position

C

CPR

Start CPR
30 chest compressions, 2 breaths

Continue CPR
Until help arrives or patient recovers

D

DEFIBRILLATION

Apply defibrillator (if available)
Follow voice prompts

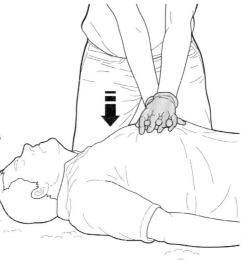

LEARN FIRST AID | 1300 360 455 | WWW.STJOHN.ORG.AU

ANAPHYLAXIS

WARNING
Anaphylaxis is a severe allergic reaction and potentially life-threatening – always treat it as a medical emergency

SIGNS & SYMPTOMS

Watch for any one of the following for anaphylaxis:

- Difficulty and/or noisy breathing
- Swelling of the tongue
- Swelling/tightness of the throat
- Difficulty talking and/or hoarse voice
- Wheezing and/or coughing
- Persistent dizziness or collapse – young children may be pale and floppy

Mild to moderate allergic reaction (may precede anaphylaxis):

- Swelling of the lips face, eyes
- Hives or welts
- Tingling mouth
- Abdominal pain and vomiting

WHAT TO DO

UNCONSCIOUS PATIENT

1. Follow DRSABCD (see page 182).
2. Immediately administer the adrenaline auto-injector, if available.

CONSCIOUS PATIENT

1. Follow DRSABCD (see page 182).
2. Help patient sit or lie in a position that assists breathing.
3. **If the patient is carrying an auto-injector (e.g. Epipen®, AnaPen®), it should be used at once. Let the patient administer the auto-injector themselves, or ask if they require assistance.**
4. Keep the patient in a lying or sitting position. Observe and record pulse and breathing.
5. **If no response after 5 minutes, further adrenaline may be given.**

SEE WWW.ALLERGY.ORG.AU FOR FURTHER INFORMATION.

BITES & STINGS

WHAT TO DO

PRESSURE BANDAGE WITH IMMOBILISATION

SEE SNAKEBITE FIRST AID (PAGE 52)

For bites/stings from: **funnel-web and mouse spiders, snakes, blue-ringed octopuses, cone shells and sea snakes.**

1. **Follow DRSABCD (see page 182).**
2. **Calm patient and keep still.**
3. **Apply a crepe bandage over the bite site.**
4. Firmly apply a heavy crepe pressure bandage, starting at the fingers/toes and working up as far as possible.
5. Immobilise the limb using splints.
6. Ensure an ambulance has been called.

ICEPACK (COLD COMPRESS)

For bites/stings from: **redback spiders bees, European wasps, ants, ticks, scorpions and centipedes.**

1. Apply an icepack directly over the bite site to relieve the pain.
2. Seek medical attention if necessary.

HOT WATER

For bites/stings from: **bluebottle (Indo-Pacific man-o'-war), jellyfish, catfish, crown-of-thorns starfish, bullrout, stingray, stonefishes and non-tropical minor jellyfish.**

1. Follow DRSABCD (see page 182).
2. Calm patient.
3. Place patient's stung limb in hot water (as hot as you, the first aider, can tolerate).
4. Ensure an ambulance has been called.

VINEGAR

For bites/stings from: **box, irukandji and jimble jellyfish, sea anemones and tropical marine stings of unknown origin.**

1. **Follow DRSABCD (see page 182).**
2. **Calm patient.**
3. **Flood stung area with vinegar for at least 30 seconds.**
4. **If vinegar is not available, flick tentacles off using a stick or gloved fingers.**
5. **Ensure an ambulance has been called.**

SEVERE BLEEDING

WHAT TO DO

UNCONSCIOUS PATIENT

1. Follow DRSABCD (see page 182).

CONSCIOUS PATIENT

1. Follow DRSABCD (see page 182).

2. Lie the patient down and remove or cut their clothing to expose the wound.

3. **Apply direct pressure over the wound using a pad or your hands (use gloves if available). Instruct the casualty to do this if possible.**

4. Squeeze the wound edges together if possible.

5. **Raise and support the injured part above the level of the heart. Handle gently if you suspect a fracture.**

6. Apply a pad over the wound if not already in place and secure by bandaging over the padded wound.

7. **If bleeding is still not controlled, leave initial pad in place and apply a second pad and secure with a bandage.**

8. **Check circulation below wound.**

9. **Ensure an ambulance has been called.**

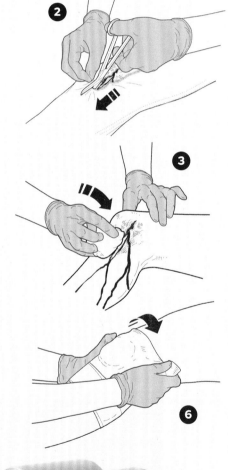

SHOCK & TRAUMA

SIGNS & SYMPTOMS

There may be little evidence of shock immediately, though symptoms can develop depending on injury severity, fluid loss and effectiveness of management. Symptoms include: weak, rapid pulse; cold, clammy skin; rapid breathing; faintness/dizziness; nausea; pale face, fingernails, lips.

WHAT TO DO

1. Follow DRSABCD (see page 182) and manage injuries such as severe bleeding (see page 186).

2. Reassure the patient.

3. Raise the patient's legs (unless fractured or a snakebite) above the level of the heart, with head flat on the floor.

4. Treat any other wounds or burns, and immobilise fractures.

5. Loosen tight clothing.

6. Maintain the patient's body warmth with a blanket or similar. DO NOT use any source of direct heat.

7. Give small, frequent amounts of water to the conscious patient who does not have abdominal trauma and who is unlikely to require an operation in the immediate future.

8. Monitor and record breathing, pulse and skin colour at regular intervals.

9. Place the patient in the recovery position if there is difficulty breathing, if patient becomes unconscious or if patient is likely to vomit.

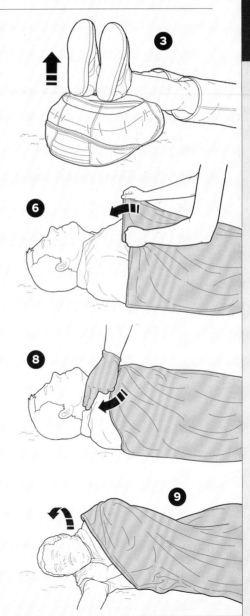

SHOCK

FIRST AID

GENERAL INDEX

A

Adders, *see Death adders*
Adrenaline 184
Aitken, Kelvin 107
Allergy 184
AnaPen 184
Anemones 176, **176**
Anaphylaxis 181, 184
Anticoagulants 18
Antivenom 17, 20, 31, 33, 40, 43, 49
Anscomb, Robin 87, 91
Ants
    Bull ant 86, **86**, 87, **87**
    Jumper ant **82**, 86, 87
    First person **87**
    First aid 185
Asian tiger mosquito 93, 94
Atlantic Portuguese man-o'-war . . 128, **128**, 129
Australian giant centipede 76, **77**, 81
Australian Pesticides and Veterinary Medicines
    Authority 95
Australian Venom Research Unit 51
Auto-injector 184

B

Banded frogfish 146
Banded sea urchin 178
Barkly Tableland death adder 37
Barmah Forest virus 95
Bastard dory 146
Beaked sea snake 155
Bees 81, **82**
    European honeybee **84**, 85
    First aid 185
Biting reef worm 166
Black house spiders 72
    Large black house spider 72, **73**
    Small black house spider 72
Black rock scorpion 76
Black sea urchin 178
Black snakes 26
    Collett's snake 26, 29, **29**
    Eastern dwarf mulga snake 26
    King brown or mulga snake 26, **27**, 28
    Mulga or king brown snake 26, **27**, 28
    Papuan black snake 26
    Red-bellied black snake 26, **28**, 29, 80
    Spotted mulga snake 26
    Spotted or blue-bellied black snake 26
    Western pygmy mulga snake 26
Black tiger snake, *see Tiger snake*
Black-tipped whaler 113
Blade fire coral **160**, 161
Blood loss 186
Blotched fantail ray 162
Blue pointer 112, **112**

Blue Mountains funnel-web 56, 58
Blue-bellied black snake 26
Blue-black sea urchin 178
Bluebottles, *see Jellyfish*
Blue-lined octopus 150, **151**
Blue-ringed octopuses **98**, 150, 159
    Blue-lined octopus 150, 151, **151**
    Greater blue-ringed octopus 98
    Southern blue-ringed octopus 150
    First aid 182, 185
Bluespotted maskray **148**, 162, 164, **164**
Bonito shark 112, **112**
Box jellyfish 121, 122, **123**, 126, **158**, 159
    First aid 185
Brazilian wandering spiders 68, **69**
Breakbone fever 93
Bristle worms 166
Broad-headed snakes 40
    Broad-headed snake 40, 42, **42**
    Lake Cronin snake 31
    Pale-headed snake 40, 43, **43**
    Stephen's banded snake 40, **43**
    Bronze whaler 113, **113**
Brown snakes 23
    Dugite 23
    Strap-snouted brown snake 23
    Speckled brown snake **22**, 23, 24
    Peninsula brown snake 23
    Ingram's brown snake 23
    Western brown snake 23, **24**, 25
    Gwardar 23, **24**, 25
    Mengden's brown snake 23, **24**, 25
    Ringed brown snake 23
    Northern brown snake 23
    Eastern (common) brown snake 23, **24**, 25, 51,
                                                  51, 81, **81**
    First aid 52
Brown tree snake 19
Bull ant 86, **86**, 87, **87**
Bull shark 102, **102**, 159, **159**
Bullrout 141
Butterfly cod **136**, **140**, 141
Byrne, Daryl 119

C

Carukia barnesi 124
Cat cone 153
Caterpillars 88, 89
    Stinging caterpillar 88, **88**
    Chinese junk 88
    Cup moth caterpillar **88**
    Slug caterpillar **88**
    Spitfire **88**
    Tussock moth caterpillar 89
    Processionary caterpillar 89
    Hairy Mary 89, **89**

Catfishes 142, **143**, **144**, 185
Centipedes 76
 Australian giant centipede 76, **77**
 First aid 185
Chinese junk. 88
Cloth of gold cone shell 153
Coastal taipan **32**, 33, 34
Cocktail shark. 113
Collector urchin. 178
Collett's snake. 26, **28**, 29
Colubrid snakes 19
Common brown snake . 23, **24**, 25, 51, **51**, 81, **81**
Common death adder 37, 39, **39**
Common octopuses. **170**, 171
Cone snail **152**, 153
Cone shells 153, 159
 Cat cone 153
 Cone snail. 153
 Geographer (Geography)cone snail. . **152**, 153
 Striated cone 153
 Textile (cloth of gold) cone 153
 Tulip cone. 153
 First aid 185
Conger, *see Eels*
Connellan, Ian 7
Convict surgeonfish. 146, **146**
Copper shark. 113
Copperheads. 45
 Lowlands copperhead 45, 46, **46**
 Highlands copperhead. **44**, 45, 46, **46**
 Dwarf (pygmy) copperhead 45
Corals, *see Fire corals*
CPR 183
Crocodiles. 115
 Freshwater or Johnstone's crocodile . 115, 116,
 117, **117**, 119
 First person. 119
 Saltwater or estuarine crocodile. . .**endpapers**,
 114, 115, 116, **116**, 118, 159
Crocodile safety. 118
Crown-of-thorns starfish. 178
Cubozoans 122
Cup moth caterpillar **88**
Cypress sea fern 156, **156**

D
Death adders. 37
 Common death adder. 37, 39, **39**
 Barkly Tableland death adder 37
 Kimberley death adder 37
 Desert death adder. 37, 38, **38**
 Northern death adder. **36**, 37
 Papuan death adder. 37
 Pilbara death adder 37
 First aid 52
Deepwater stargazer. 146

DEET 95
Demon stinger 141
Dengue fever 83, 92, 93
Desert death adder. 37, 38, **38**
Desert scorpion 76
Devil scorpionfish 141
Diadema 178
Double-spined sea urchin. 178
DRSABCD first aid action plan. 182
Duck-billed platypus **96**, 97
Dugite 23
Dwarf (pygmy) copperhead. 45

E
Eastern brown snake .**16**, 23, **24**, 25, 51, **51**, 81, **81**
Eastern dwarf mulga snake 26
Eastern mouse spider. 64, 65, **65**
Eastern small-eyed snake 30, **30**
Eels. 173
 Giant moray **172**, 173
 Whitemouth moray. 173
 Southern conger 173
Electric rays. 165
Emergency telephone numbers 4
Epipen 184
Estuarine crocodile. . **114**, 115, 116, **116**, 118, 159
Estuarine stonefish. .138
Estuary shark. 102
Estuary stingray 162
European honeybee, *see Bees*
Eyestripe surgeonfish. 146

F
False stonefish. 141
Fenner, Dr Peter. 6
Fire corals 161
 Blade fire coral. **160**, 161
 First aid 161
Fire jelly. 122
Fire urchin. 178, **179**
First aid
 Adrenaline 184
 Allergy. 184
 AnaPen 184
 Anaphylaxis 184
 Auto-injector. 184
 Bites. 181, 185
 Bleeding, severe 186, 187
 Cardiopulmonary resuscitation 183
 CPR 183
 DRSABCD action plan 182, 183
 Epipen. 184
 Shock 181, 183, 187
 Stings. 185
 Trauma 187
 First aid by cause
 Bluebottles. 129, 130, 131

GENERAL INDEX

Fire corals 161
Irukandji 125
Platypus 97
Snakes 52, 53
Spiders 74, 75
Ticks 78
For all other creatures see page 185
First aid kit 181
Fishes, venomous 137
  Banded frogfish 146
  Bastard dory 146
  Bullrout 141
  Butterfly cod, or red lionfish **140**, 141
  Catfishes 142, **143, 144, 145,** 185
  Convict surgeonfish 146, **146**
  Deepwater stargazer 146
  Demon stinger 141
  Devil scorpionfish, or false stonefish 141
  Estuarine stonefish 138
  Eyestripe surgeonfish 146
  Fortescue 141
  Fringed stargazer 146
  Frogfish 146
  Golden-lined spinefoot 146, **147**
  Marbled spinefoot 146
  Ocellated waspfish 141
  Old wife 146, **147**
  Rabbitfish 146
  Reef stonefish 138, **139**
  Scorpionfishes 141
  Spotted scorpionfish 141
  Unicornfish 146
  First aid 185
Flower urchin 178
Fortescue 141
Freshwater crocodile 115, 116, 117, **117,** 119
Freshwater whaler 102
Fringed stargazer 146
Frogfish 146
Funnel-web spiders 56, 68
  Funnel-web spiders 56, **60**
  Sydney funnel-web 56, **57,** 58, **59,** 80
  Blue Mountains funnel-web 56, 58
  Northern tree/Northern Rivers funnel-web 56
  Toowoomba funnel-web 56
  Victorian funnel-web 56
  First aid 74, 75, 185

G
Garden wolf spider 67
Geographer/Geography cone snail **152**, 153
Giant moray **172**, 173
Giant Queensland groper/cod **174**, 175
Golden fireworm 166
Golden-lined spinefoot 146
Greater blue-ringed octopus **98**, 150

Great white shark 104, **104**, 159
Grey nurse shark 107, **107**
Gropers 175
  Giant Queensland groper/cod **174**, 175
  Southern Australian bass groper 175
  Spotted cod 175
Guillain-Barré syndrome 94
Gwardar 23, **25**

H
Haemotoxins 18
Hairy caterpillars 89, **89**
Hairy Mary 89, **89**
Hell's fire anemone 176
Highlands copperhead **44**, 45, 46, **46**
Hives 184
Honeybee, *see Bees*

I
Indo-Pacific Portuguese man-o'-war 129
Ingram's brown snake 23
Inland taipan 33, **34,** 35, 81
Insects 83
Irukandji 124, **125,** 126, 127, 129, 159
Irukandji syndrome 124, 125

J
Jack-jumper 86
Japanese encephalitis 94
Jellyfish 120
  Atlantic Portuguese man-o'-war 128, **128,** 129
  Bluebottles 129, 159
  Box jellyfish 121, 122, **122,** 126, **158,** 159
  Fire jelly 122
  Indo-Pacific Portuguese man-o'-war 129
  Irukandji 124, **123,** 125, 126, 159
  Jelly blubber **120,** 132
  Jimble/Lantern medusa 127
  Lion's mane jellyfish 132, **133**
  Mauve stinger 132
  Moon/saucer jelly 132, **134**
  Morbakka 122
  Sea wasp 122, 127
  South-western stinger 127
  Stinging sea nettle 132
  First aid 125, 129, 130, 131, 185
Jelly blubber **120,** 132
Jimble/Lantern medusa 127, **127**
Johnstone's crocodile 115, 116, **116, 117,** 119
Jumper ant **82,** 86, 87

K
Keelback snake 47
Kimberley death adder 37
King brown or mulga snake 26, **27,** 28

L
Lake Cronin snake 31

Lantern medusa 127
Large black housespider 72, **73**
Leopard shark 110
Lesser red-headed mouse spider 64
Lionfish, *see Fishes, venomous*
Lion's name jellyfish 132, **133**
Longfin waspfish 141
Long-spined sea urchin 178
Lowlands copperhead 45, 46, **46**

M
Maguire, Kylie 111
Mako sharks, *see Sharks*
Malaria, *see Mosquitoes*
Man-o'-war *see Jellyfish*
Mantis shrimp 177, **177**
Marbled spinefoot 146
Mauve stinger 132
Mengden's brown snake 23, **24**, 25
Millipedes 76
Moon/saucer jelly 132, **134**
Morbakka 122
Morays, *see Eels*
Mosquitoes 71, 92, 93, 94, 95
  Aedes 92, 94
  Aedes aegypti 92, 94
  Aedes albopictus 93, 94, **94**
  Anopheles 92, 93
  Anopheles farauti **92**
  Asian tiger mosquito 93, 94
  Culex 92, 94
  Culex annulirostris 94
  Guillain-Barré syndrome 94
  Malaria 71, 92, 93
  Murray Valley encephalitis 94
  Prevention (of bites) 95
  Ross River fever 83, 94
  Zika virus 94
Mouse spiders 64
  Eastern mouse spider 64, 65, **65**
  Red-headed mouse spider 64
  Lesser red-headed mouse spider 64
  First aid 75, 185
Mulga or king brown snake 26, **27**, 28
Murray Valley encephalitis 94
Mygalomorph spiders, *see Mouse spiders*
Myotoxins 18

N
Necrosis 70
Nematocysts 121, 122, 130
Neurotoxins 18
Northern brown snake 23
Northern death adder **36**, 37
Northern Rivers funnel-web 56
Northern tree funnel-web 56

Numbfish 165
Numb rays 165

O
Ocellated waspfish 141
Oceanic whitetip shark 108, **108**
Oceanic whitetipped whaler 108, **108**
Octopuses 171
  Common octopus **170**, 171
  See Blue-ringed octopus
Old wife 146, **147**
Olive sea snake 154, **154**, 155

P
Pacific octopus 171
Pale-headed snake 40, 43, **43**
Paper wasps 90, **90**, 91, **91**
  First person 91
Papuan black snake 26
Papuan death adder 37
Paralysis ticks 78
  Australian paralysis tick 78, **78**, 80, 81
  Tasmanian paralysis tick 78
  First aid 78, 185
  First person 79
Peninsula brown snake 23
Picaridin 95
Pilbara death adder 37
Pit vipers 19
Platypus **96**, 97
Porcupine ray 162
Portuguese man-o'-war, *see Jellyfish*
Pressure bandages 53, 75, 185
Processionary caterpillar 89
Purple sea urchin 178
Pygmy copperhead 45

R
Rabbitfish, *see Fishes, venomous*
Rays, *see Stingrays*
Redback spider ......title page, 62, **63**, 74, 75, 81
  First aid 74, 75, 185
Red-bellied black snake 26, **28**, 29, 80
Red-headed mouse spider 64
Reef stonefish 138, **138**
Ringed brown snake 23
Riverwhaler 102
Ross River fever 94
Rough-scaled snake 47

S
Saltwater crocodile . . **114**, 115, 116, **116**, 118, 159
Sambono, Joe 49
Scientific names 13
Scorpionfishes, *see Fishes, venomous*
Scorpions 76
  Marbled scorpion **5**, 76

GENERAL INDEX

Black rock scorpion 76
Desert scorpion .76, **76**
Wood (forest) scorpion 76
First aid 185
Sea anemones 176
Hell's fire anemone 176
Sea snakes 155
Beaked sea snake 155
Olive sea snake 154, **154**, 155
Stokes' sea snake 155
Yellow-bellied sea snake 155, 159
Sea urchins 178
Banded sea urchin 178
Black sea urchin 178
Blue-black sea urchin 178
Collector urchin 178
Crown-of-thorns starfish 178
Diadema 178
Double-spined sea urchin 178
Fire urchin 178, **178**
Flower urchin 178
Long-spined sea urchin 178
Purple sea urchin 178
Spiny sea urchin 178
Tam o' shanter urchin 178
Sea wasp 121, 122, 127
Segmented worms 166
Biting reef worm 166
Bristle worm 166
Golden fireworm 166, **167**
Southern seamouse 166
Sergeant ant 86
Seymour, Jamie 126
Shark attack 106, 107, 111
Sharks 101
Black-tipped whaler 113, **113**
Blue pointer **100**, 112, **112**
Bonito shark **100**, 112, **112**
Bronze whaler 113, **113**
Bull shark 101, 102, **103**, 159
Cocktail shark 113, **113**
Copper shark 113, **113**
Estuary shark 102, **103**
Freshwater whaler 102, **102**
Great white shark . . . . title page, 104, **104**, 159
Grey nurse shark 107, **107**
Leopard shark 110, **110**, 159
Mackerel shark **100**, 112, **112**
Man-eater shark 110, **110**, 159
Oceanic whitetip shark 108, **108**
Oceanic whitetipped whaler 108, **108**
Riverwhaler 102, **103**, 159
Shortfin mako **100**, 112, **112**
Snapper shark **100**, 112, **112**
Tiger shark 110, **110**, 159
White death . . . . title page, 104, **104**, 159

White pointer . . . . . . title page, 104, **104**, **105**
Whitetip whaler 108, **108**
Zambezi shark 102, **102**
First person 107, 111
Shock 187
Shortfin mako shark **100**, 112, **112**
Slug caterpiller 88
Small black house spider 72
Small-eyed snakes 30
Smooth stingray 162, **163**
Snakes, *see under*
Black snakes
Broad-headed snakes
Brown snakes
Copperheads
Death adders
Rough-scaled snake
Sea snakes
Small-eyed snakes
Tiger snake
Taipans
Snake scales 21
Snake venoms 18, 20
Snake bite mechanics 19
First aid 52, 185
First person 31, 49
Snake safety 50
Snakes, venomous 17
Fangs 19
First aid 52
Snapper shark 112, **112**
Southern Australian bass groper 175
Southern blue-ringed octopus 150
Southern conger 173
South-western stinger 127
Speckled brown snake 23
Spinefoot, *see Fishes, venomous*
Spiny sea urchin 178
Spiders *see under*
Black house spider
Funnel-web spider
Mouse spider
Redback spider
White-tailed spider
Wolf spider
First aid 74, 75, 185
Sponges 168
Spotted or blue-bellied black snake 26
Spotted cod 175
Spotted mulga snake 26
Spotted scorpionfish 141
Starfish, *see Sea urchins*
Stephen's banded snake 40, **40**
Stevens, Austin J. 10, **11**
Stingaree 162
Stinging caterpillars 88, **88**

Stinging hydroids 156
  Cypress seafern 156, **156**
  White stinging seafern 156
Stinging sea nettle 132
Stingrays 162
  Blotched fantail ray 162
  Bluespotted maskray **148**, 162, 164, **164**
  Estuary stingray .162
  Porcupine ray 162
  Smooth stingray 162, **163**
  Stingaree 162
  First aid 185
Stokes's sea snake 155
Striated cone 153
Stonefishes 138
  Reef stonefish 138, **138**
  Estuarine stonefish 138
  First aid 138
Strap-snouted brown snake 23
Striped catfishes 142, **142**, **144**
Surgeonfish 146
Sydney funnel-web 56, **57**, 58, **59**, 80

T
Taipans 33
  Coastal taipan **32**, 33, 34, **34**
  Inland taipan 33, **34**, 35, 81
  Western desert taipan 33, **34**, 35
  First aid 52, 53
Tam-o'-shanter sea urchin 178
Textile or cloth of gold cone 153
Ticks, *see Paralysis ticks*
Tiger shark 110, **110**, 159
Tiger snake 48, **48**, 81
Toowoomba funnel-web 56
Torpedofish 165
Trapdoor spiders, *see Mouse spiders*
Trauma 187
Tulip cone 153
Tussock moth caterpillar 89

U
Unicornfish 146
Union Jack spiders 67

V
Victorian funnel-web 56
Vipers 19

W
Wasps 90
  First aid 185
Webb, Dr Cameron 95
Western brown snake 23, **24**, 25
Western desert taipan 33, **34**, 35
Western pygmy mulga snake 26
White death, *see Sharks: great white shark*

White pointer, *see Sharks: great white shark*
White stinging seafern 156
White-tailed spider 70
Whitemouth moray .173
Wilson, Steve K 7, 31
Wolf spiders 66, **66**, 67
  Wolf spider 66, **66**, 67
  Garden wolfs 67
  Union Jack spiders 67
Wood (forest) scorpion 76
World Health Organization 71, 93
Worms, *see Segmented worms*

Y
Yellow-bellied sea snake 155, 159

Z
Zambesi shark 102
Zborowski, Paul 7
Zika virus 94

SCIENTIFIC NAME INDEX

Acanthaster planci 178
Acanthophis 37
Acanthophis antarcticus 37, 39, 51
Acanthophis hawkei 37
Acanthophis lancasteri 37
Acanthophis praelongus 37
Acanthophis pyrrhus 37, 38
Acanthophis rugosus 37
Acanthophis wellsi 37
Acanthuridae 146
Acanthurus dussumieri 146
Acanthurus triostegus 146
Acarina 78
Actinodendron arboreum 176
Actinopodidae 64
Adamsia 176
Aedes 92, 94
Aedes aegypti 92, 94
Aedes albopictus 93
Aglaophenia cupressina 156, 157
Aipysurus laevis 154, 155
Alatina alata 124
Alatinidae 124
Anemonia 13, 176
Anopheles 92
Anopheles farauti 92
Anthelidae 89
Anthozoa 176
Aphrodita australis 166

SCIENTIFIC NAME INDEX

Apidae 85
Apis mellifera 81, 84, 85
Apistur carinatus 141
Arachnida 55
Araeosoma ijimai 178
Ariidae 142
Asthenosoma varium 178, 179
Astrotia stokesii 155
Atrax robustus 56, 57, 58, 59, 60, 68, 74, 80
Aurelia aurita 132, 134
Austrelaps 45
Austrelaps labialis 45
Austrelaps ramsayi 45, 46, 47
Austrelaps superbus 45, 46, 47
Badumna 72
Badumna insignis 72
Badumna longinqua 72
Batrachoides spp. 146
Batrachoididae 146
Calliactis 176
Carcharhiniforme 101
Carcharhinus brachyurus 113
Carcharhinus leucas 102, 159
Carcharhinus longimanus 108
Carcharias taurus 107
Carcharodon carcharias 104, 159
Carukia barnesi 124
Carukia shinju 124
Carukiidae 124
Carybdea marsupialis 122
Carybdea rastoni 127
Carybdea xaymacana 127
Carybdeidae 122, 127
Catostylus mosaicus 132
Centropogon australis 141
Centrostephanus rodgersii 178
Cephalopoda 171
Cercophonius squama 76
Chilopoda 76
Chirodropidae 122
Chironex fleckeri 121, 122, 123, 126
Chloeia flava 166, 167
Chrysaora quinquecirrha 132
Cnidaria 121
Colubridae 17
Conger verreauxi 173
Congridae 173
Conidae 153
Conus catus 153
Conus geographus 153
Conus striatus 153
Conus textile 153
Conus tulipa 153
Crocodilia 115
Crocodylus 116
Crocodylus johnstoni 116, 117

Crocodylus porosus 13, 116, 159
Cryptophis 30
Cryptophis nigrescens 30
Culex 92, 94
Culex annulorostris 94
Culicidae 92
Cyanea capillata 132, 133
Dasyatididae 162
Dasyatis brevicaudata 162, 163
Dasyatis fluviorum 162
Diadema savignyi 178
Diadema setosum 178
Echinoidea 178
Echinothrix calamaris 178
Echinothrix diadema 178
Elapidae 17, 31, 155
Enhydrina schistosa 155
Enoplosidae 146
Enoplosus armatus 146
Enteroctopus dofleini 171
Epinephelus lanceolatus 174, 175
Ethmostigmus rubripes 76, 77, 81
Eunice aphroditois 166
Eurythoe complanata 166
Galeocerdo cuvier 110, 159
Gymnothorax javanicus 172, 173
Gymnothorax meleagris 173
Gymnuridae 56
Hadronyche formidabilis 56
Hadronyche infensa 56
Hadronyche modesta 56
Hadronyche versuta 56, 58
Halophryne diemensis 146
Hapalochlaena spp. 150, 159
Hapalochlaena fasciata 150, 151
Hapalochlaena lunulata 150
Hapalochlaena maculosa 150
Heliocidaris erythrogramma 178
Hexathelidae 56
Hoplocephalus 31, 40
Hoplocephalus bitorquatus 40, 43
Hoplocephalus bungaroides 40, 42
Hoplocephalus stephensii 40, 41
Hydrophiinae 155
Hydrozoa 161
Ichthyscopus barbatus 146
Inimicus caledonicus 141
Inimicus didactylus 141
Isurus oxyrinchus 100, 112
Ixodes cornuatus 78
Ixodes holocyclus 78
Kathetostoma nigrofasciatum 146
Keesingia gigas 124
Lactodectus hasselti 81
Lamniforme 101, 104
Lampona 70

Lampona cylindrata 70
Lampona murina 70
Latrodectus hasselti 62, 74, 75, 81
Lebrunia 176
Limacodidae 88
Lissodendoryx spp. 168
Lychas marmoreus 76
Lycosa godeffroyi 67
Lycosidae 67
Lycosa godeffroyi 67
Lymantriidae 89
Lytocarpus philippinus 156
Malo bella 124
Malo kingi 124
Malo maximus 124
Millepora platyphylla 160, 161
Missulena bradleyi 64
Missulena insignis 64
Missulena occatoria 64, 65
Morbakka fenneri 124
Muraenidae 173
Mycobacterium ulcerans 70
Myliobatidae 162
Myrmecia 80, 86
Neofibularia irata 168
Neofibularia mordens 168
Neotrygon kuhlii 162
Netuma spp. 142
Nolidae 89
Notechis 48, 81
Notechis scutatus 48, 81
Notesthes robusta 141
Notodontidae 89
Octopus vulgaris 170, 171
Ornithorhynchus anatinus 97
Oxyuranus 33
Oxyuranus microlepidotus 33, 35
Oxyuranus scutellatus 33, 34
Oxyuranus temporalis 33, 35
Paroplocephalus atriceps 31
Pelagia noctiluca 132
Pelamis platurus 155, 159
Phoneutria spp. 68
Physalia 129
Physalia physalis 128, 129, 159
Physalia utriculus 129
Physobrachia 176
Plasmodium 93
Plectropomus maculatus 175
Plotosidae 142
Plotosus lineatus 142, 144
Plotosus spp. 142
Plumulariidae 156
Polistes 90
Polistes humilis 90
Polistinae 90

Polychaeta 166
Polyprion moeone 175
Porifera 168
Pseudechis 26
Pseudechis australis 26, 28
Pseudechis butleri 26
Pseudechis colletti 26, 29
Pseudechis guttatus 26
Pseudechis pailsii 26
Pseudechis papuanus 26
Pseudechis porphyriacus 26, 80
Pseudechis weigeli 26
Pseudonaja 23
Pseudonaja affinis 23
Pseudonaja aspidorhyncha 23
Pseudonaja guttata 23, 24
Pseudonaja inframacula 23
Pseudonaja ingrami 23
Pseudonaja mengdeni 23, 25
Pseudonaja modesta 23
Pseudonaja nuchalis 23
Pseudonaja textilis 23, 25, 81
Pteroisantennata 141
Pterois volitans 140, 141
Physobrachia 176
Rattus villosissimus 35
Rhizostomeae 132
Ropalidia 90
Sagartia 176
Scorpaena plumieri 141
Scorpaenidae 138, 141
Scorpaenopsis diabolus 141
Scorpionida 76
Semaeostomeae 132
Serranidae 175
Siganidae 146
Siganus lineatus 146
Siganus rivulatus 146
Stomatopoda 177
Synanceia horrida 138
Synanceia verrucosa 138
Tachysurus spp. 142
Taeniura meyeni 162
Tamoyidae 124
Toxopneustes pileolus 178
Tripneustes gratilla 178
Tropidechis 47
Tropidechis carinatus 47
Tropidonophis mairii 47
Uranoscopidae 146
Urodacus manicatus 76
Urodacus yaschenkoi 76
Urogymnus asperrimus 162
Urolophidae 162
Vespidae 90
Vespula 90

PHOTOGRAPHER/ILLUSTRATOR CREDITS

Andy Murch/OceanwideImages 113
Anthony Calvert 53, 75, 131, 181, 182, 183, 186, 187
Arco Images GmbH/Alamy Stock Photo 97, 147
Auscape/Contributor/Getty 54, 78, 119
Auscape/UIG/Getty 117
Auscape/UIG/REX/Shutterstock 159
Australian Geographic 71
Australian Museum 65
Barry Skipsey/Australian Geographic 118
Birgitte Wilms/Minden Pictures/Getty 177
Brendan Schembri 32, 51, 51
C & M Fallows/OceanwideImages 112
Chris Hay 35
Claude Thivierge 19
Courtesy Austin Stevens 11
Dave Watts/Alamy Stock Photo 96
David Hancock/Australian Geographic 114, 159
David Maitland/Getty 75
Denis Crawford 82, 82
Don Fuchs/Australian Geographic 50
Dr Peter Fenner 6
Esther Beaton/Australian Geographic 14, 57, 59, 60, 63, 66, 68, 70, 74
F1online digitale Bildagentur GmbH/ Alamy Stock Photo 170
FLPA/Alamy Stock Photo 152, 159
Franco Banfi/Getty 159, 167
Gary Bell/OceanwideImages 66, 123, 125, 127, 139, 142, 147, 154, 157, 159, 164, 165, 169, 174, 179
Georgette Douwma/NPL 176
Graphic Science/Alamy Stock Photo 88, 89
Ian Connellan 7
Ian Waldie/Staff/Getty 63
imageBROKER/Alamy Stock Photo 159, 160
James Pozarik/Australian Geographic 18, 20

Jeff Hunter/Getty 172
Jeff Rotman/Getty 152
Jeff Wildermuth/Getty 134
Joe Sambono 49
Kelvin Aitken 6, 104, 107, 108
Kristian Bell/Getty 16
Marjorie Crosby-Fairall/ Australian Geographic 109
Matthew Smith 128
Michael Patrick O'Neill/OceanwideImages 103
Minden Pictures/Alamy Stock Photo 120
Museums Victoria half title
National Geographic Creative/ Alamy Stock Photo 65, 69
Nick Rains/Australian Geographic 158
Nick Volpe 44, 48, 51, 76, 77, 81
OceanwideImages 47, 100
Paul Zborowski 5, 7, 70, 73, 79, 80, 84, 86, 87, 90, 91
PeteKaras/Getty 13
Peter Parks/Getty 111
Ralph Alphonso/Australian Geographic 93
Reinhard Dirscherl/Alamy Stock Photo 144
Richard Thwaites/Australian Geographic End papers
Rob Valentic 51
Shutterstock Full title, 9, 52, 94, 95, 98, 109, 110, 116, 130, 136, 140, 148, 151, 159, 164, 180, 184, 185, 186
Simeon Scott / Alamy Stock Photo 73
Stephen Zozaya 36, 51
Steve Brennan / Newspix 126
Steve Wilson 7, 9, 21, 22, 24, 27, 28, 29, 30, 31, 38, 39, 41, 42, 43, 46, 51, 81
Stewart Macdonald 25, 34, 51
WaterFrame/Alamy Stock Photo 133, 159, 163